TEACHER'S GUIDE 2B

Noogol

Googol

Koogol

Ooogol

Toogol

Zoogol

Consultant and author
Dr Fong Ho Kheong

Authors
Chelvi Ramakrishnan and Michelle Choo

UK consultants
Carole Skinner, Simon d'Angelo and Elizabeth Gibbs

OXFORD
UNIVERSITY PRESS

Published by Marshall Cavendish Education
Times Centre, 1 New Industrial Road, Singapore 536196
Customer Service Hotline: (65) 6213 9444
Email: tmesales@mceducation.com
Website: www.mceducation.com

Distributed by
Oxford University Press
Great Clarendon Street, Oxford,
OX2 6DP, United Kingdom
www.oxfordprimary.co.uk
www.oxfordowl.co.uk

First published 2015
Reprinted 2015

ISBN 978-981-01-3118-0

Printed in China

Acknowledgements
Written by Dr Fong Ho Kheong, Chelvi Ramakrishnan and Michelle Choo

UK consultants: Carole Skinner, Simon d'Angelo and Elizabeth Gibbs

Cover artwork by Daron Parton

The authors and publisher would like to thank all schools and individuals who
helped to trial and review Inspire Maths resources.

Contents

The background to *Inspire Maths*

A letter from Dr Fong Ho Kheong

Dear Colleague,

I am both humbled and proud to see that my work has now been adapted for use in many countries. *My Pals are Here!*, the series from which *Inspire Maths* is adapted, has been translated into languages including Spanish, Indonesian, Dutch and Arabic, and the books are used by millions of children all over the world.

International surveys show that children taught with the series score higher than their peers in standardised tests, and also that it helps young children to become more confident with maths. The 2012 PISA survey again placed Singapore's children at the top of international rankings for mathematics; the country also had the highest percentage of top achievers. In the USA, it was reported in 2013 that schools in the Fayette County, West Virginia who had adopted the programme had made impressive progress in their mathematics results, including a 12 per cent improvement among third graders in one school and a 20 per cent improvement among fourth graders in another.

Why does *Inspire Maths* work? A major strength of *Inspire Maths* is its robust structure, based on best-practice principles and methods of teaching and learning mathematics, including the concrete-pictorial-abstract (CPA) and scaffolding approaches, and a systematic teaching pathway. This comprehensive pathway emphasises mastery – with continuous, active reinforcement of concepts to help children assimilate and accommodate their learning – followed by extension, challenging children to develop and practise the thinking skills that will enable them to become confident, critically aware and independent learners. The textbooks from which *Inspire Maths* is adapted have also been informed by continuous evaluation of their success in the classroom, through a process of school visits, classroom observation and programme review. Because of this, *Inspire Maths* gives you a proven framework for supporting children of all abilities to achieve success.

Inspire Maths is based on well-established constructivist ideas of learning, and the views of internationally-renowned educationalists including Jerome Bruner, Jean Piaget, Lev Vygotsky, Richard Skemp and David Ausubel. Constructivism underpins the programme's approach to learning mathematical concepts and skills through assimilation and accommodation, and their reinforcement through reflective activities such as journal writing and error correction. This perspective is also reflected in the programme's emphasis on mastery learning and building children's confidence.

More particularly, Bruner's three modes of representation are mirrored by the concrete–pictorial–abstract learning progression which is central to *Inspire Maths*. Bruner's ideas parallel Piaget's stages of development; essentially, children's understanding of mathematical concepts depends on their stage of development. Learning in the early stages is achieved through concrete representation. Then, when ready, children can move on to pictorial representations – such as the bar model – which in turn provide them with a bridge to the abstract stage, and a flexible, fully independent understanding of the abstract, symbolic language of maths. Though it cannot be used to tackle every problem, the bar model has a particularly significant role in helping children at the concrete and semi-concrete operational stage (Piaget's developmental theory) to approach and solve problems successfully.

Skemp's ideas about instrumental and relational understanding are also an important part of the pedagogy underpinning *Inspire Maths*. Skemp suggests that learning mathematics by relating ideas to each other (relational understanding) is more meaningful, and therefore more effective, than memorising facts and procedures (instrumental understanding). Building on these ideas, *Inspire Maths* is designed to develop children's lasting and profound mathematical understanding which they will continue to extend and apply.

I would like to congratulate the UK schools and teachers who have made the choice to use *Inspire Maths*. I am confident that your children will experience similar success to that seen in other countries who have adopted this approach.

Dr Fong

Dr Fong achieved a PhD in Mathematics Education from King's College London before teaching mathematics in the National Institute of Education, Nanyang Technological University, for over 24 years. He is currently a senior Mathematics Specialist with the Regional Centre for Education in Science and Mathematics (RECSAM) in Penang, Malaysia. He has published more than 100 journal articles, research reports, and primary and secondary mathematics books, and his research work includes diagnosing children with mathematical difficulties and teaching thinking skills to solve mathematical problems.

What is *Inspire Maths?*

Inspire Maths is the UK edition of *My Pals are Here!*, the internationally renowned approach used to teach maths in Singapore, which was heavily influenced by the Cockroft report of 1982[1]. Singapore's Ministry of Education drew on leading international research on effective teaching and learning of mathematics to meet the challenge of raising primary mathematics attainment within Singapore's schools.

The approach to mathematics teaching and learning that was developed was further refined over subsequent decades and it is this approach that is central to *My Pals are Here!* Authored by Dr Fong Ho Kheong and first published in 2001, *My Pals are Here!* is used by almost 100% of State Primary schools and over 80% of Primary schools in Singapore.

Dr Fong's overarching aim in developing *My Pals are Here!* was to help all children understand and use mathematics confidently and competently, and to support non-specialist maths teachers to deliver this. The programme's success in achieving this aim is reflected in the high levels of mathematics attainment by Singapore's pupils, who are consistently ranked among the very top in international comparison studies such as PISA and TIMSS. It is also reflected in the results of schools outside Singapore that have adopted the series, for example, in the USA and South Africa.

Inspire Maths provides a highly scaffolded learning framework with problem solving at its heart. It is built on a focused, coherent and cumulative spiral curriculum that continuously builds and consolidates knowledge to reach deep understanding. The programme encourages extensive practice to develop fluency and mastery, so that every child – across all abilities – can succeed at mathematics.

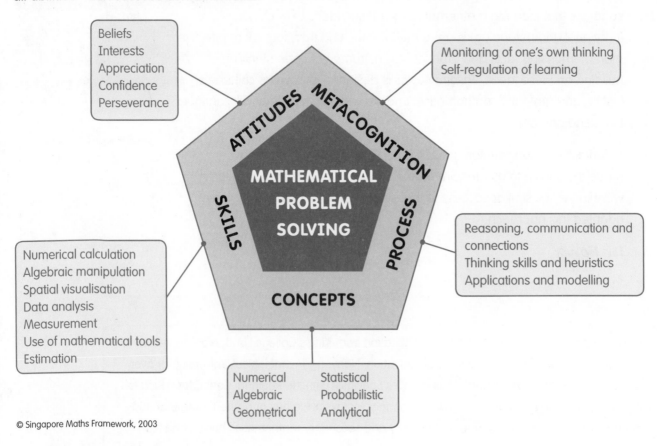

Beliefs
Interests
Appreciation
Confidence
Perseverance

Monitoring of one's own thinking
Self-regulation of learning

ATTITUDES METACOGNITION

MATHEMATICAL PROBLEM SOLVING

SKILLS

PROCESS

CONCEPTS

Numerical calculation
Algebraic manipulation
Spatial visualisation
Data analysis
Measurement
Use of mathematical tools
Estimation

Reasoning, communication and connections
Thinking skills and heuristics
Applications and modelling

Numerical	Statistical
Algebraic	Probabilistic
Geometrical	Analytical

© Singapore Maths Framework, 2003

The principles that underpin *Inspire Maths*

1   *Mathematics Counts*, Dr W.H.Cockroft, 1982

The concrete-pictorial-abstract approach

Inspire Maths emphasises the development of critical thinking and problem solving skills, which help children make connections to develop deeper understanding. The powerful concrete–pictorial–abstract (CPA) approach, including the bar model method, is central to this.

Why is the CPA approach so powerful? From very early on in their school life, we expect children to use and understand numbers, which are abstract concepts. Many children struggle with this and so their first experiences of mathematics can be confusing, leaving them with no solid foundation to build on for later learning. The CPA approach helps children achieve secure number sense – that is, a sense of what numbers really represent and how to use them mathematically. This is done through a series of carefully structured representations – first using physical objects (concrete), then diagrams or pictures (pictorial), and ultimately using representations such as numerals (abstract).

In the example below from *Inspire Maths* Pupil Textbook 2A, children are exploring subtraction within 1000. Using the CPA approach, they explore with base ten equipment, then using a picture of base ten in a place value chart, and finally through words, written symbols and calculations.

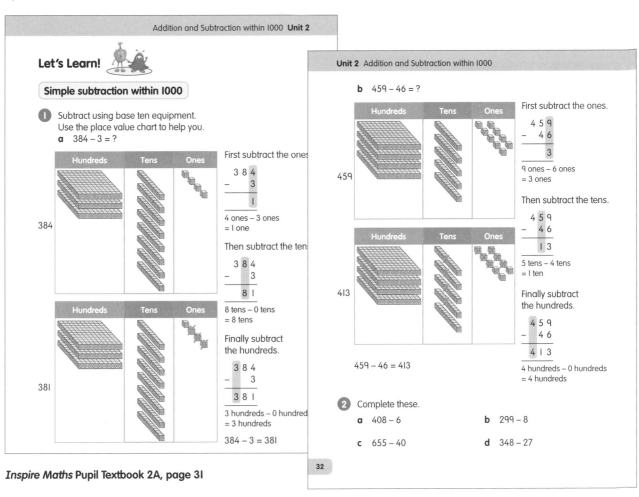

Inspire Maths **Pupil Textbook 2A, page 31**

Inspire Maths **Pupil Textbook 2A, page 32**

The bar model

The bar model is a step-by-step method that helps children to understand and extract the information within a calculation or word problem. By drawing a bar model, children translate a calculation or word problem into a picture. The approach helps children process the information given in the problem, visualise the structure, make connections and solve the problem.

The bar model is first introduced in *Inspire Maths* 2. In the following activity, children explore addition and subtraction initially with concrete apparatus before moving on to using a pictorial representation – the bar model.

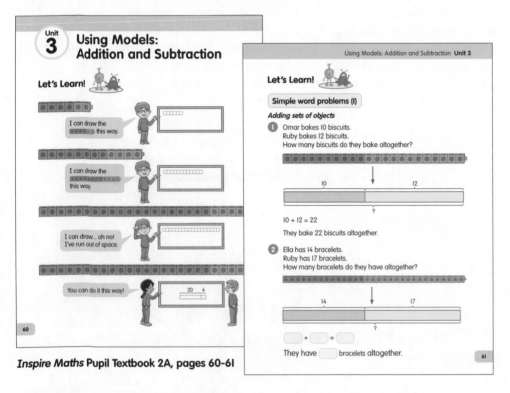

Inspire Maths Pupil Textbook 2A, pages 60-61

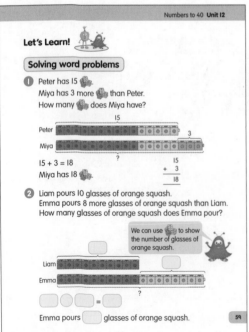

Inspire Maths Pupil Textbook 1B, page 59

In *Inspire Maths* 1, children have been prepared for the introduction of the bar model by using concrete apparatus; for example, using interlocking cubes to compare the number of objects in two groups.

Heuristics for problem solving

Inspire Maths helps children learn to use *heuristics* to solve problems. *Heuristics* refers to the different strategies that children can adopt to solve unfamiliar or non-routine problems. These strategies include drawing the bar model, pattern-spotting, using diagrams and estimating or 'guess and check'.

In this example from *Inspire Maths* Pupil Textbook 2A, children are encouraged to draw diagrams to solve the problems.

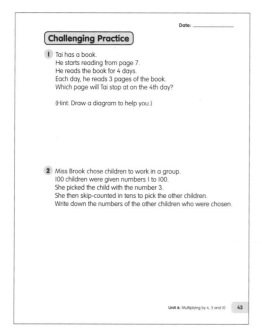

Inspire Maths Practice Book 2B, page 43

Inspire Maths Pupil Textbook 2A, page 131

The *Inspire Maths* Practice Books reinforce concepts introduced in the Pupil Textbooks and provide varied, frequent practice to develop fluency. As they practise, children begin to self-select the appropriate strategy for each problem, helping them to become confident problem solvers.

Higher-order questioning

Inspire Maths is designed to stimulate thinking beyond the activities from the Pupil Textbooks. The activities should kick-start mathematically meaningful conversations through questioning, giving children opportunities to think mathematically, discover connections and be creative.

You can use written problems as a starting point for further questioning, for example, when presented with 7 + 4 = 11 and an accompanying bar model, you might ask, 'What would happen if it was 11 – 4? Or 11 – 7? What about 7 + 4 or 4 + 7?' Then take it further: 'What would the bar model look like if it was 8 + 4?'

Modelling higher-order questioning at every opportunity will encourage children to use this strategy to explore and solve problems for themselves.

Making use of variation

Research shows that mathematical and perceptual variation deepens understanding as it constantly challenges children to develop their existing understanding by looking at questions from different perspectives and adapting to new situations. The numbers and problems in *Inspire Maths* activities have been specifically selected on this basis to challenge children as the questions progress and lead them towards mastery.

Mathematical variation

With mathematical variation, the mathematical concept, for example addition, stays the same but the variation is in the mathematics. For example, addition *without* regrouping and addition *with* regrouping. The variation challenges children to use their mathematical skills flexibly to suit the situation, deepening understanding.

Perceptual variation

With perceptual variation, the mathematical concept is the same throughout the sequence of questions but is presented in different ways. In this example from *Inspire Maths* Pupil Textbook 2A, perceptual variation in place value is provided by the use of base ten equipment alongside numbers in words and numerals, leading to a deeper understanding.

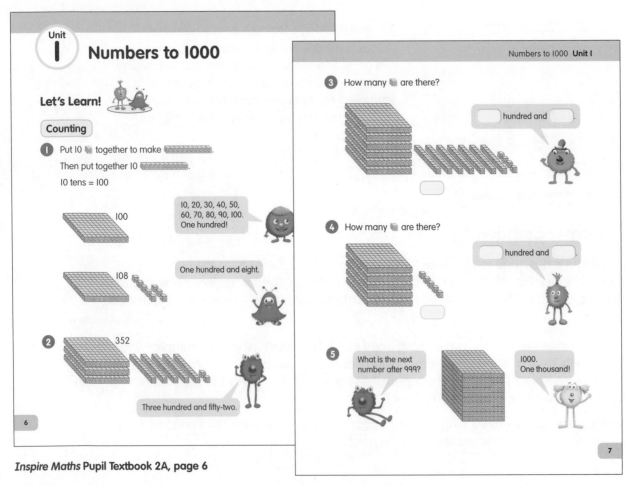

Inspire Maths Pupil Textbook 2A, page 6

Inspire Maths Pupil Textbook 2A, page 7

The *Inspire Maths* teaching pathway

Inspire Maths is a programme that teaches to mastery. It is built on a cumulative spiral curriculum, focusing on core topics to build deep understanding. The *Inspire Maths* teaching pathway scaffolds in-depth learning of key mathematical concepts through the development of problem-solving and critical thinking skills, and extensive opportunities for practice.

Pupil Textbooks to scaffold new learning

Inspire Maths Pupil Textbooks present new learning clearly and consistently, providing a highly scaffolded framework to support all children. Mathematical concepts are presented visually, with specific and structured activities, to build firm foundations. There are two Pupil Textbooks for each level.

Let's Learn! to build firm foundations

Carefully scaffolded learning through *Let's Learn!* activities in the *Inspire Maths* Pupil Textbooks promotes deep mathematical understanding through:

- clearly presented pages to illustrate how the CPA approach can be used to build firm foundations

- careful questioning to support the use of concrete apparatus

- opportunities for higher-order questioning (see page ix) to help children become confident and competent problem solvers

- opportunities to assess each child's understanding and prior knowledge through observing their use of concrete apparatus and how they approach the activity

- use of mathematical talk to explore and develop reasoning skills.

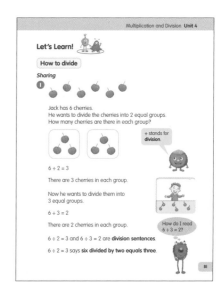

Inspire Maths Pupil Textbook 2A, page 81

Guided practice to develop deep understanding

After a concept has been introduced in *Let's Learn!*, guided practice develops the deep understanding required for mastery. Support and guide children as they work collaboratively in pairs or small groups through the guided practice activities indicated by empty coloured boxes in the Pupil Textbook.

Frequent opportunities for guided practice:
- help children develop deep understanding

- develop mathematical language and reasoning through collaborative work

- provide further opportunities to check children's understanding by observing their use of concrete apparatus and listening to their discussions

- help you to provide appropriate intervention – guiding those who need extra support and challenging those who are ready for the next step.

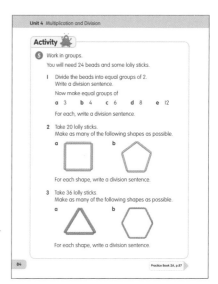

Inspire Maths Pupil Textbook 2A, page 84

Let's Explore! and *Games* to investigate and apply learning

Engaging games and investigative *Let's Explore!* activities in the *Inspire Maths* Pupil Textbooks encourage children to apply concepts they have been learning and provide an opportunity to assess their reasoning skills by observing how they approach the tasks.

Children work collaboratively in small groups or pairs:

- games reinforce skills, concepts and problem solving strategies leading to mastery

- *Let's Explore!* activities encourage children to investigate connections through mathematical reasoning

- meaningful discussion and conversation develop mathematical language.

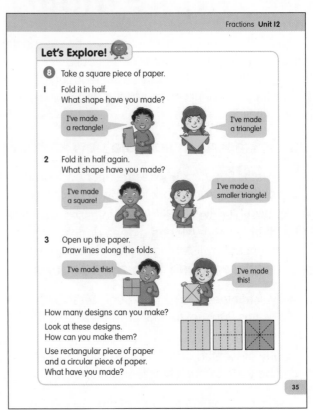

Inspire Maths Pupil Textbook 2B, Page 35

Maths Journal to reflect

The *Maths Journal* is where each child records their mathematical thinking and reflects on their learning. The typical Maths Journal would be a child's own exercise book or notebook – something that the child 'owns', can share with you, with parents or carers, and that builds up over time.

Children reflect on their learning through their Maths Journal:

- giving both the child and you a valuable assessment tool, showing progress over time

- providing opportunities for children to discuss their thinking with each other, parents or carers, and with you, helping to establish next steps and giving a sense of pride in their achievements.

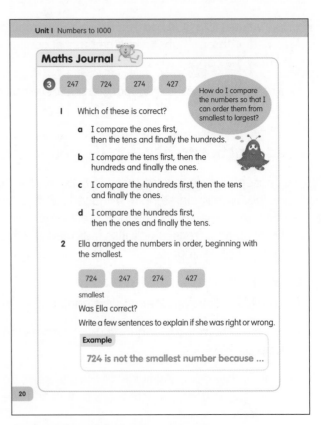

Inspire Maths Pupil Textbook 2A, Page 20

Put on Your Thinking Caps! to challenge

Each unit concludes with a *Put on Your Thinking Caps!* activity in the Pupil Textbook which challenges children to solve non-routine problems.

Challenging activities:

- ask children to draw on prior knowledge as well as newly learned concepts

- ask children to use problem solving strategies and critical thinking skills, for example sequencing or comparing

- provide valuable opportunities to assess whether children have developed a deep understanding of a concept by listening to their explanations of their mathematical thinking and looking at how they model the problem, for example using concrete apparatus and pictorial representations.

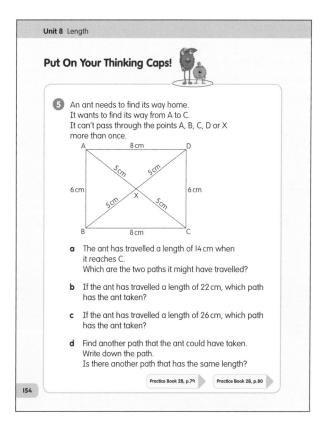

Inspire Maths Pupil Textbook 2A, page 154

Home Maths to encourage mathematical conversations

Home maths activities in the Pupil Textbooks are engaging, hands-on suggestions that parents and carers can use with children to explore maths further outside the classroom, for example through finding shapes in pictures and around the house.

Engaging home activities:

- help you to involve parents and carers in their child's mathematical learning

- help children to see maths in the world around them.

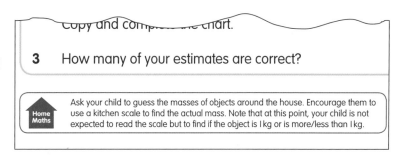

Inspire Maths Pupil Textbook 2A, page 157

Practice Books to develop fluency and consolidate

Inspire Maths Practice Books provide carefully structured questions to reinforce concepts introduced in the Pupil Textbooks and to provide varied, frequent practice. A wealth of activities develop fluency, build mathematical confidence and lead towards mastery. The Practice Books are also a valuable record of individual progress. There are four Practice Books for *Inspire Maths* 1-3 and two Practice Books for *Inspire Maths* 4-6.

Each Practice Book includes:

- **Challenging Practice** and **Problem Solving** activities to develop children's critical thinking skills

- **Reviews** after every two or three units, to reinforce learning

- **Revisions** that draw from a range of preceding topics, concepts and strands, for more complete consolidation.

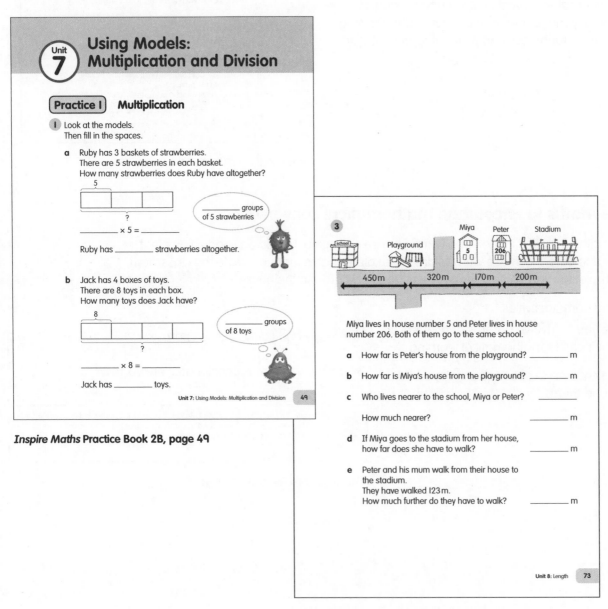

Inspire Maths **Practice Book 2B, page 49**

Inspire Maths **Practice Book 2B, page 73**

Assessment Books to create a record of progress

Inspire Maths provides comprehensive Assessment Books with regular summative assessments to create a record of progress for each child, as well as giving children opportunities to reflect on their own learning. The wraparound assessment provided through the *Inspire Maths* teaching pathway in combination with the *Inspire Maths* Assessment Books enables rapid, appropriate intervention as soon as a child needs it, before they fall behind and when they are ready to be challenged. Topics and concepts are frequently revisited in the assessments, helping to build mastery.

There is one Assessment Book for each level, providing complete coverage of the key concepts across a year. Each assessment is divided into sections so you can easily break them down into appropriate chunks to suit your class. For the early levels, you may choose to assess in small groups, reading out the questions and scribing answers. Encourage children to use concrete apparatus when they need support to help them work through the questions.

There are three types of assessment within each Assessment Book:

1. **Main assessments:** The main assessments cover the key learning objectives from the preceding two or three units of the Pupil Textbooks. Through the main assessments, children are given opportunities to apply their learning in a variety of different contexts, helping you to quickly identify which children are ready to move on and which need further support. Children may self-mark to reflect on their progress.

2. **Check-ups:** There are four check-ups for each level which revisit the previous units, drawing on prior knowledge to encourage children to make connections and apply their learning to solve problems. These assessments give you valuable opportunities to check children's understanding through observing how they approach questions, use and interpret mathematical language and use heuristics.

3. **Challenging Problems:** These assessments make use of non-routine and unfamiliar questions to see how children use their repertoire of strategies to tackle more challenging problems. Use this as an opportunity to assess children's mathematical thinking, reasoning and problem solving skills by looking at their methods and how they approach the problem. They are particularly suitable for extension and assessing a child's level of mastery.

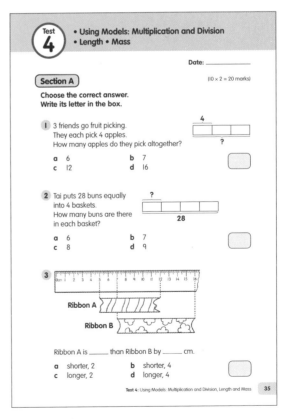

Inspire Maths Assessment Book 2, page 35

Using the Teacher's Guide

Key concepts clearly outline the important ideas children will be introduced to within each unit.

There are two *Inspire Maths* Teacher's Guides for each level, one per Pupil Textbook. Each Teacher's Guide contains:

- information on how to get started
- long-term planning support
- medium-term planning support
- suggested teaching sequence for each pupil textbook page
- answers
- photocopiable activities.

Learning objectives clearly signal the aims of the unit, which are designed to help children develop their understanding of the unit's key concepts. Children are introduced to the learning objectives in the Pupil Textbook. The Practice Book provides opportunities to practise and consolidate for mastery.

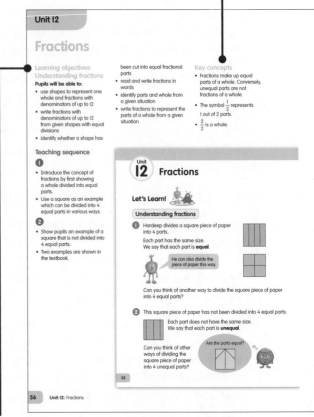

Inspire Maths Teacher's Guide 2B, pages 56-57

Opportunities are flagged for children to work independently in their **Maths Journal**, to record and reflect on their learning, leading towards mastery.

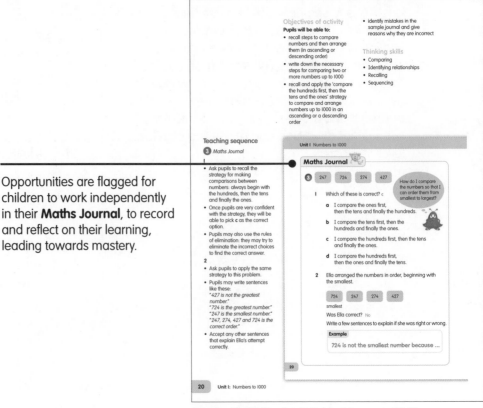

Inspire Maths Teacher's Guide 2A, pages 20-21

Key thinking skills and problem solving strategies to look for and encourage are clearly highlighted, helping you to make meaningful assessments of children's understanding.

Ideas for **further practice activities** to develop fluency are outlined in every unit.

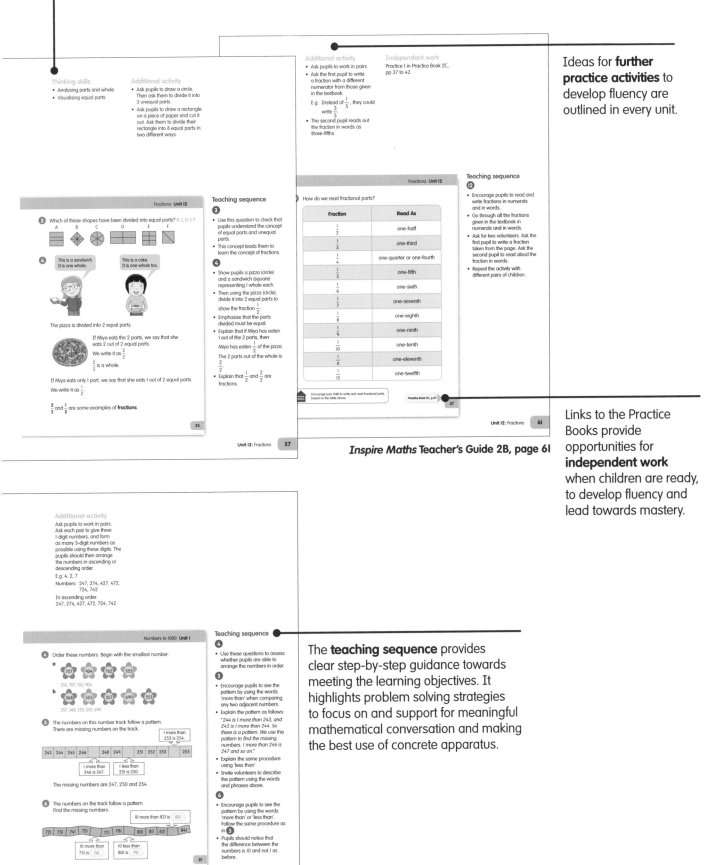

Inspire Maths Teacher's Guide 2B, page 61

Links to the Practice Books provide opportunities for **independent work** when children are ready, to develop fluency and lead towards mastery.

The **teaching sequence** provides clear step-by-step guidance towards meeting the learning objectives. It highlights problem solving strategies to focus on and support for meaningful mathematical conversation and making the best use of concrete apparatus.

Long-term planning

Unit title	Key concepts
1 Numbers to 1000	
Counting	• Counting numbers up to 1000 by using concrete representations • Strategies for counting in ones, tens and hundreds
Place value	• Each digit of a number has its own value
Comparing numbers within 1000	• Identify the place and value of the digits of corresponding numbers and then compare
Order and pattern	• Numbers are said to form a pattern when they are arranged in a systematic order. To find the next number in a pattern, we add or subtract a certain fixed number
2 Addition and Subtraction within 1000	
Simple addition within 1000	• The 'adding on' concept is related to calculation in addition • The digit at each place has its own value
Simple subtraction within 1000	• The 'taking away' concept is related to calculation in subtraction • The digit at each place has its own value
Addition with regrouping the ones	• The regrouping concept in addition
Addition with regrouping the tens	
Addition with regrouping the tens and ones	
Subtraction with regrouping the tens and ones	• The regrouping concept in subtraction
Subtraction with regrouping the hundreds and tens	• Regrouping in hundreds and tens in subtraction
Subtraction with regrouping the hundreds, tens and ones	• Regrouping in hundreds, tens and ones in subtraction
Subtraction with numbers that have zeros	• Regrouping involving zeros in hundreds to tens and tens to ones
Practice Book – Review 1	
Assessment Book – Test 1	
3 Using Models: Addition and Subtraction	
Simple word problems (1)	• Using models to find the whole from two or more parts • Using models to find a part of a whole
Simple word problems (2)	• Using models to make a whole by joining one or more parts to another • Using models to show when one or more sets are taken away
Simple word problems (3)	• The 'comparing' concept can be represented by models
Two-step word problems	• Using model drawings to represent various concepts in addition and subtraction when solving problems
4 Multiplication and Division	
How to multiply	• Multiplication is conceptualised as multiplying a fixed number of objects by a certain number of times. The fixed number of objects refers to the number of objects in a group. The number of groups refers to the number of times it is multiplied
How to divide	• Division is conceptualised as sharing or dividing a set of items into equal groups so that each group has the same number of items
Practice Book – Review 2	
Assessment Book – Test 2, Challenging Problems 1, Check-up 1	

Unit title	Key concepts
5 Multiplying by 2 and 3	
Multiplying by 2: skip-counting	• Multiplication is interpreted as repeated addition and as groups of items
Multiplying by 2: using dot paper	• The 'relating facts' concept can be used to find a more difficult multiplication fact using dot paper
Multiplying by 3: skip-counting	• Multiplication is interpreted as repeated addition and as groups of items
Multiplying by 3: using dot paper	• The 'relating facts' concept can be used to find a more difficult multiplication fact using dot paper
Division	• Division is the inverse of multiplication
6 Multiplying by 4, 5 and 10	
Multiplying by 4: skip-counting	• Multiplication is conceptualised as repeated addition, groups of items, or multiplying
Multiplying by 4: using dot paper	• The 'group and number of items in each group' concept is applied
Multiplying by 5: skip-counting	• Multiplication is conceptualised as groups of items and as sequential numbers in the 'skip-counting' strategy
Multiplying by 5: using dot paper	• The 'group and number of items in each group' concept is applied
Multiplying by 10: skip-counting and using dot paper	• Multiplication is interpreted as groups of items and as sequential numbers in the 'skip-counting' strategy
Division	• Division is conceptualised as the inverse of multiplication and as the equal sharing of items
Practice Book – Review 3	
Assessment Book – Test 3	
7 Using Models: Multiplication and Division	
Multiplication	• Multiplication is conceptualised as the total number of items, given groups of items
Division	• Division is conceptualised as sharing or dividing a set of items into equal groups so that each group has the same number of items
8 Length	
Measuring in metres	• Length is a concept of measurement to determine how long or short an object is • The metre (m) is a unit of measurement for length
Comparing lengths in metres	• The metre is a medium for measuring and comparing
Measuring in centimetres	• Length is a concept of measurement to determine how long or short an object is • The centimetre (cm) is a unit of measurement for length
Comparing lengths in centimetres	• The centimetre is used to measure and compare the lengths of two or more objects
Addition and subtraction of length	• The 'addition' and 'subtraction of numbers' concepts and techniques are applied in this section

Unit title	Key concepts
Multiplication and division of length	• The 'multiplication' and 'division' concepts in numbers are applied in this section
9 Mass	
Measuring in kilograms	• The kilogram (kg) is a unit of measurement for mass
Comparing masses in kilograms	• The kilogram (kg) is used as a medium to find the masses of objects and compare masses
Measuring in grams	• The gram (g) is a unit of measurement for mass
Comparing masses in grams	• An object can be heavier or lighter than another based on the masses of the two objects
Addition and subtraction of mass	• The process of addition and subtraction of mass is similar to addition and subtraction of whole numbers
Multiplication and division of mass	• Pupils can use concepts in multiplication and division to solve multiplication and division problems
Practice Book – Revision 1	
Assessment Book – Test 4, Challenging Problems 2, Check-up 2	
10 Mental Calculations	
Mental addition	• Using number bonds in mental addition
Mental subtraction	• Using number bonds in mental subtraction
11 Money	
Counting pounds and pence	• The dot separates the pounds from the pence
Changing pounds and pence	• £1 = 100p • When changing pence to pounds, use the dot to separate the pounds from the pence • When changing pounds to pence, remove the dot from the pounds
Comparing amounts of money	• Comparing amounts of money by comparing the pounds followed by the pence
Word problems	• Solving one-step or two-step word problems involving money using addition and subtraction • Solving one-step or two-step word problems involving money using multiplication and division
Practice Book – Review 4	
Assessment Book – Test 5	
12 Fractions	
Understanding fractions	• Fractions make up equal parts of a whole. Conversely, unequal parts are not fractions of a whole • The symbol $\frac{1}{2}$ represents 1 out of 2 parts • $\frac{2}{2}$ is a whole
More fractions	• Using modelling as a concept to represent fraction contexts
Comparing and ordering fractions	• Quantifying and comparing fractions

Unit title	Key concepts
Adding and subtracting like fractions	• Quantifying, adding and subtracting fractions
Solving word problems	• Applying the 'adding on', 'taking away', 'part-whole' and comparing concepts in solving word problems involving fractions
13 Time	
The minute hand	• The minute is a measure of time • The minute hand of the clock is used to indicate the time in minutes
Reading and writing the time	• Hours and minutes are measures of time
Learning a.m. and p.m.	• Time is told in a.m. and p.m. • 'a.m.' is used for time after 12 midnight to just before 12 noon • 'p.m.' is used for time after 12 noon to just before 12 midnight
Time taken in hours and minutes	• 'Hour' is written as h and 'minutes' is written as mins • Time taken between two given times is measured in h and mins
Practice Book – Review 5	
Assessment Book – Test 6, Challenging Problems 3, Check-up 3	
14 Volume	
Getting to know volume	• The capacity of a container is the amount of space it can hold • The volume of a container is the amount of space it contains
Measuring in litres	• The litre (ℓ) is a unit of measurement for volume
Addition and subtraction of volumes	• Volume in litres can be added and subtracted like whole numbers
Multiplication and division of volumes	• Volume in litres can be multiplied and divided like whole numbers
15 Graphs	
Reading picture graphs	• Picture graphs represented by symbols can be compared and interpreted
Making picture graphs	• Picture graphs can be made using different symbols and scales
More graphs	• Interpreting picture graphs to solve problems
Practice Book – Review 6	
Assessment Book – Test 7	
16 Lines and Surfaces	
Straight lines and curves	• Represent lengths with straight lines • Interpret straight lines with given lengths
Flat surfaces	• Identifying flat surfaces and curved surfaces
17 Shapes and Patterns	
2D shapes	• Identifying semicircles and quarter circles
3D shapes	• Shapes can be visualised as 3D shapes
Making patterns	• Patterns are made by repeating sequences
Practice Book – Revision 2	
Assessment Book – Test 8, Challenging Problems 4, Check-up 4	

Week	Learning Objectives	Thinking Skills	Resources
I	**(1) Mental addition** Pupils will be able to: • use number bonds for 10s to mentally add a 1-digit number to a 2-digit number within 100 without regrouping • use number bonds to mentally add a 1-digit number to a 3-digit number with or without regrouping the ones • use number bonds to mentally add a 3-digit number and tens with or without regrouping in tens • use number bonds to mentally add a 3-digit number and hundreds without regrouping in hundreds	• Classifying • Identifying patterns and relationships	• Pupil Textbook 2B, pp 6 to 12 • Practice Book 2C, pp 5 to 8 • Teacher's Guide 2B, pp 4 to 10

Week	Learning Objectives	Thinking Skills	Resources
1	**(2) Mental subtraction** Pupils will be able to: • use number bonds to mentally subtract a 1-digit number from a 2-digit number within 100 with or without regrouping • use number bonds to mentally subtract a 1-digit number from a 3-digit number within 1000 with or without regrouping the tens into ones • use number bonds to mentally subtract tens from a 3-digit number within 1000 with or without regrouping the hundreds into tens • use number bonds to mentally subtract hundreds from a 3-digit number without regrouping	• Identifying patterns and relationships	• Pupil Textbook 2B, pp 13 to 18 • Practice Book 2C, pp 9 to 10 • Teacher's Guide 2B, pp 11 to 16

Mental Calculations

Learning objectives: Mental addition

Pupils will be able to:

- use number bonds for 10s to mentally add a 1-digit number to a 2-digit number within 100 without regrouping
- use number bonds to mentally add a 1-digit number to a 3-digit number with or without regrouping in ones
- use number bonds to mentally add a 3-digit number and tens with or without regrouping in tens
- use number bonds to mentally add a 3-digit number and hundreds without regrouping in hundreds

Key concept

Using number bonds in mental addition

Teaching sequence

- Revise number bonds involving tens and the 'part-whole' concept with numbers less than or equal to 10. Explain the method involving number bonds for tens.

  E.g. 8-2—10 :
  "Adding 8 is the same as adding 10 and subtracting 2."

  7-3—10:
  "Adding 7 is the same as adding 10 and subtracting 3."

- Use this method to help pupils to add 58 and 8 mentally:
  "Adding 8 to 58 is the same as adding 10 to 58 (= 68) and then subtracting 2 which is 68 – 2 = 66."

- Look out for pupils who can add 9 to 76.

❸

- Use this question to check that pupils understand the method above. You can explain as follows:
  "Adding 6 is the same as adding 10 and subtracting 4."
  "Adding 9 is the same as adding 10 and subtracting 1."

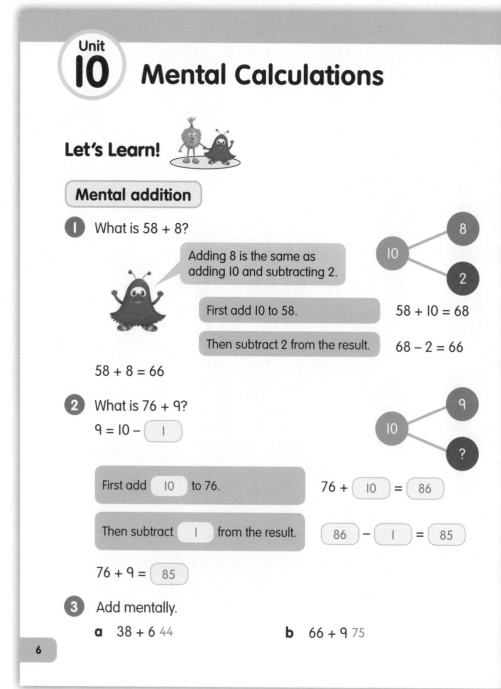

Thinking skills
- Classifying
- Identifying patterns and relationships

What you will need
- A dice
- Cards with numbers 6, 7, 8 and 9 (see Photocopy master 1 on p 249)

Game

4 **Add mentally!**
How to play:

Players: 2 to 4
You will need:
- a dice
- cards with numbers 6, 7, 8 and 9

1 Player 1 rolls the dice two times to make a two-digit number.

2 Player 1 draws a card to get another number.

3 Player 1 adds the two numbers mentally.

26 + 7 = ?

4 The other players check the answer. Get 1 point for each correct answer.

26 + 7 = 33

5 Take turns to play. Play ten rounds.

The player with the most points wins!

7

Teaching sequence

4 *Game*

- Ask pupils to follow the steps in the textbook.
- Pupils will need to master mental addition using the method shown in **1** and **2**.

Ask pupils to work in pairs.

Pupil A calls out a 3-digit number.

Pupil B calls out a I-digit number so that the total of the ones digits for the two numbers is less than I0.

Pupil A mentally adds the numbers and then their partner checks the answer.

Pupils A and B swap roles.

Teaching sequence

- Revise addition of two I-digit numbers without regrouping.
- Show pupils some examples of number bonds for numbers less than I0.

  E.g. 5-3—8

      6-2—8

      5-2—7

      3-4—7

- Ask pupils to add from left to right, and at the same time mentally add the ones in the two numbers.

  (a) Mentally add 3 and 6 to get 9.

  (b) Read from left to right: 253 and 6 gives 259.

- Look for pupils who can add 5 to 472.
- Guide pupils by showing that 2 and 5 gives 7; therefore by reading from left to right, they should find: 472 + 5 = 477

- Ask pupils to practise adding these mentally.

  "Adding 7 to 2 gives 9."

  "Adding 5 to 4 gives 9."

Unit I0 Mental Calculations

5 What is 253 + 6?

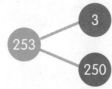

First add the ones.   3 + 6 = 9

Then add the result to the hundreds, tens and ones.   250 + 9 = 259

253 + 6 = 259

6 What is 472 + 5?

First add the ones.   2 + 5 = 7

Then add the result to the hundreds, tens and ones.   470 + 7 = 477

472 + 5 = 477

7 Add mentally.

  a 322 + 7 329   **b** 414 + 5 419

8

Ask pupils to work in pairs.

Pupil A calls out a 3-digit number.

Pupil B calls out a I-digit number. The ones digits for the two numbers must add up to 10 or more.

Pupil A mentally adds the numbers and then their partner checks the answer.

Pupils A and B swap roles.

Mental Calculations **Unit 10**

8 What is 128 + 4?

Adding 4 is the same as adding 10 and subtracting 6.

$4 = 10 - 6$

First add 10 to 128. $128 + 10 = 138$

Then subtract 6 from the result. $138 - 6 = 132$

$128 + 4 = 132$

9 What is 347 + 8?

$8 = 10 - \boxed{2}$

First add $\boxed{10}$ to 347. $347 + \boxed{10} = \boxed{357}$

Then subtract $\boxed{2}$ from the result. $\boxed{357} - \boxed{2} = \boxed{355}$

$347 + 8 = \boxed{355}$

10 Add mentally.

a 156 + 7 163

b 243 + 9 252

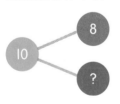
Point out to your child that **5** to **7** do not involve regrouping while **8** to **10** do involve regrouping. Discuss how the methods differ.

Teaching sequence

8

- Revise addition of two I-digit numbers with regrouping the ones. Show pupils some examples of number bonds for numbers less than 10.

  E.g. 4-6—10
        3-7—10
        2-8—10

- Show pupils the strategy to find 128 + 4:
  (a) Add 10 to 128 to get 138.
  (b) Since 6 + 4 = 10, subtract 6 from 138 to get 132.

9

- Use this question to check that pupils have understood the method.

- Encourage pupils to recall the number bond: 2-8—10

10

- Ask pupils to practise adding these mentally.

- Note the number bonds for these questions are:
  3-7—10
  1-9—10

Ask pupils to work in pairs.

Pupil A calls out a 3-digit number.

Pupil B calls out a tens number so that the total of the tens digits for the two numbers is 90 or less.

Pupil A mentally adds the numbers and then their partner checks the answer.

Pupils A and B swap roles.

Teaching sequence

- Revise addition of two 2-digit numbers without regrouping the tens.
- Show pupils some examples of number bonds involving tens.

  E.g. 50-30—80
  60-20—80
  50-20—70
  40-30—70

- Ask pupils to add from left to right and at the same time mentally add the tens from the two numbers.

  (a) Mentally add 10 and 50 to get 60.

  (b) Read from left to right: 213 and 50 gives 263.

12

- Use this question to check that pupils have understood the method above.
- Encourage pupils to recall the number bond:
  50-40—90

13

- Ask pupils to practise adding these sums mentally, using the strategy from **12**.

Unit 10 Mental Calculations

11 What is 213 + 50?

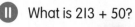

| First add the tens. | $10 + 50 = 60$ |

| Then add the result to the hundreds, tens and ones. | $203 + 60 = 263$ |

$213 + 50 = 263$

12 What is 351 + 40?

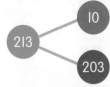

| First add the tens. | $\boxed{50} + 40 = \boxed{90}$ |

| Then add the result to the hundreds, tens and ones. | $301 + \boxed{90} = \boxed{391}$ |

$351 + 40 = \boxed{391}$

13 Add mentally.

  a 247 + 50 297

  b 613 + 70 683

10

Ask pupils to work in pairs.

Pupil A calls out a 3-digit number.

Pupil B calls out a tens number. The tens digit for the two numbers must add up to more than 90.

Pupil A mentally adds the numbers and then their partner checks the answer.

Pupils A and B swap roles.

Teaching sequence

14

- Revise addition of two 2-digit numbers with regrouping the tens.
- Show pupils some examples of number bonds in 10s.
  E.g. 30-70—100
          20-80—100
          40-60—100
- Show pupils the strategy to solve 345 + 80:
  (a) Add 100 to 345 to get 445.
  (b) Since 20 + 80 = 100, subtract 20 from 445 to get 425.

15

- Use this question to check that pupils have understood the method above.
- Encourage pupils to recall the number bond:
  10-90—100

16

- Ask pupils to practise adding these mentally using the strategy outlined above.

Mental Calculations **Unit 10**

14 What is 345 + 80?

> Adding 80 is the same as adding 100 and subtracting 20.

100
80
20

80 = 100 − 20

First add 100 to 345.   345 + 100 = 445

Then subtract 20 from the result.   445 − 20 = 425

345 + 80 = 425

15 What is 568 + 90?

90
100
?

90 = 100 − ⬚ 10

First add ⬚ 100 to 568.   568 + ⬚ 100 = ⬚ 668

Then subtract ⬚ 10 from the result.   ⬚ 668 − ⬚ 10 = ⬚ 658

568 + 90 = ⬚ 658

16 Add mentally.

a   468 + 70 538   b   795 + 40 835

> Home Maths
> Encourage your child to come up with their own addition problems and to show how they solve them.

II

Ask pupils to work in pairs.

Pupil A calls out a 3-digit number.

Pupil B calls out a hundreds number so that the total of the hundrends digit for the two numbers is less than 1000.

Pupil A mentally adds the numbers and then their partner checks the answer.

Pupils A and B swap roles.

Practice I in Practice Book 2C, pp 5 to 8.

Teaching sequence

- Revise addition of a 3-digit number and hundreds without regrouping the hundreds.
- Show pupils some examples of number bonds in hundreds.
  E.g. 300-600—900
        300-500—800
        200-500—700
- Show pupils the strategy to solve 172 + 300.
  (a) Add 300 to 100 to get 400.
  (b) Add the tens and ones:
      400 + 72 = 472.

- Use this question to check that pupils have understood the method above.

- Ask pupils to practise adding these mentally, using the strategy outlined above.

Unit 10 Mental Calculations

17 What is 172 + 300?

172 — 100
    — 72

First add the hundreds.   100 + 300 = 400

Then add the result to the tens and ones.   72 + 400 = 472

172 + 300 = 472

18 What is 469 + 200?

469 — ?
    — 69

First add the hundreds.   400 + 200 = 600

Then add the result to the tens and ones.   69 + 600 = 669

469 + 200 = 669

19 Add mentally.

  a   492 + 300 792   b   287 + 600 887

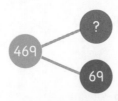

Practice Book 2C, p.5

12

Learning objectives: Mental subtraction

Pupils will be able to:

- use number bonds to mentally subtract a 1-digit number from a 2-digit number within 100 with or without regrouping
- use number bonds to mentally subtract a 1-digit number from a 3-digit number within 1000 with or without regrouping the tens into ones
- use number bonds to mentally subtract tens from a 3-digit number within 1000 with or without regrouping the hundreds into tens
- use number bonds to mentally subtract hundreds from a 3-digit number without regrouping

Key concept

Using number bonds in mental subtraction

Thinking skill

Identifying patterns and relationships

Mental Calculations **Unit 10**

Let's Learn!

Mental subtraction

1 What is 62 − 8?

Subtracting 8 is the same as subtracting 10 and adding 2.

10 — 8 / 2

First subtract 10 from 62. $62 - 10 = 52$

Then add 2 to the result. $52 + 2 = 54$

$62 - 8 = 54$

2 What is 84 − 7?

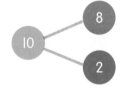
10 — 7 / ?

First subtract ⬚10⬚ from 84. $84 - \boxed{10} = \boxed{74}$

Then add ⬚3⬚ to the result. $\boxed{74} + \boxed{3} = \boxed{77}$

$84 - 7 = \boxed{77}$

3 Subtract mentally.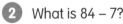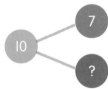

a 72 − 9 63

b 62 − 6 56

13

Teaching sequence

1

- Revise number bonds involving tens and the 'part-whole' concept with numbers less than or equal to 10. Explain the method involving number bonds for tens for subtraction.

  E.g. 2-8—10:
  "Subtracting 8 is the same as subtracting 10 and adding 2."

  1-9—10:
  "Subtracting 9 is the same as subtracting 10 and adding 1."

  3-7—10:
  "Subtracting 7 is the same as subtracting 10 and adding 3."

- Use this method to help pupils mentally subtract 8 from 62.
  (a) Subtract 10 from 62 to get 52.
  (b) Add 2 to 52 to get 54.

2

- Use this question to check pupils' understanding.
- Encourage pupils to recall the number bond: 7-3—10

3

- Ask pupils to practise subtracting these numbers mentally, using the strategy above.

Encourage pupils to practise the following number bonds:

- 49-1—50:
  Subtracting 49 → Subtract 50, add 1
- 48-2—50:
  Subtracting 48 → Subtract 50, add 2
- 47-3—50:
  Subtracting 47 → Subtract 50, add 3
- 46-4—50:
  Subtracting 46 → Subtract 50, add 4

Teaching sequence

- Revise subtraction of a 1-digit number from another 1-digit number without regrouping.
- Work through this example:
  (a) Subtract 4 from 9 to get 5.
  (b) Subtract from left to right, using the answer found in (a) above:
  429 – 4 = 425

- Use this question to check that pupils have understood the strategy above.
- Guide pupils to follow the two-step strategy.

- Ask pupils to practise subtracting these numbers mentally, using the strategy outlined above.

Unit 10 Mental Calculations

4 What is 429 – 4?

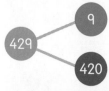

| First subtract the ones. | 9 – 4 = 5 |

| Then add the result to the hundreds, tens and ones. | 420 + 5 = 425 |

429 – 4 = 425

5 What is 748 – 5?

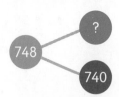

| First subtract the ones. | 8 – 5 = 3 |

| Then add the result to the hundreds, tens and ones. | 740 + 3 = 743 |

748 – 5 = 743

6 Subtract mentally.

a 437 – 3 434

b 628 – 4 624

14

Ask pupils to work in pairs.

Pupil A calls out a 3-digit number.

Pupil B calls out a I-digit number that is more than the ones from the first number.

Pupil A mentally subtracts the numbers and then their partner checks the answer.

Pupils A and B swap roles.

Mental Calculations **Unit 10**

7 What is 545 – 7?

Subtracting 7 is the same as subtracting 10 and adding 3.

 7
10
3

First subtract 10 from 545. 545 – 10 = 535

Then add 3 to the result. 535 + 3 = 538

545 – 7 = 538

8 What is 872 – 6?

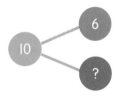
6
10
?

First subtract 10 from 872. 872 – 10 = 862

Then add 4 to the result. 862 + 4 = 866

872 – 6 = 866

9 Subtract mentally.

a 543 – 7 536

b 745 – 8 737

Home Maths Point out to your child that 4 to 6 do not involve regrouping while 7 to 9 do involve regrouping. Discuss how the methods differ.

15

Teaching sequence

7

- Revise subtraction of a I-digit number from a 2-digit number with regrouping the tens into ones.
- Revise the method involving number bonds for tens for subtraction.
- Show pupils the strategy to solve 545 – 7.
  - (a) Remind pupils of the number bond 7-3—10.
  - (b) Subtract 10 from 545 to get 535.
  - (c) Add 3 to the result to get 538.

8

- Use this question to check pupils' understanding.
- Encourage pupils to recall the number bond: 4-6—10

9

- Ask pupils to practise subtracting these numbers mentally.

Additional activity

Ask pupils to work in pairs.

Pupil A calls out a 3-digit number.

Pupil B calls out a tens number that is less than the tens from the first number.

Pupil A mentally subtracts the numbers and then their partner checks the answer.

Pupils A and B swap roles.

Teaching sequence

- Revise subtraction of tens from another tens without regrouping.
- Show pupils the strategy to solve 753 – 30.
  - (a) Identify the tens in the 3-digit number.
  - (b) Mentally subtract 30 from 50 to get 20.
  - (c) Subtract from left to right, using the answer found in (b) above:
    753 – 30 = 723

- Use this question to check that pupils have understood the strategy above.

12

- Ask pupils to subtract these numbers mentally, using the strategy outlined above.

Unit 10 Mental Calculations

10 What is 753 – 30?

| First subtract the tens. | 50 – 30 = 20 |

| Then add the result to the hundreds, tens and ones. | 703 + 20 = 723 |

753 – 30 = 723

11 What is 692 – 40?

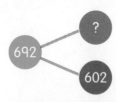

| First subtract the tens. | 90 – 40 = 50 |

| Then add the result to the hundreds, tens and ones. | 602 + 50 = 652 |

692 – 40 = 652

12 Subtract mentally.

    a   480 – 20 460   **b**   276 – 50 226

16

Additional activity

Ask pupils to work in pairs.

Pupil A calls out a 3-digit number.

Pupil B calls out a tens number that is more than the tens from the first number.

Pupil A mentally subtracts the numbers and then their partner checks the answer.

Pupils A and B swap roles.

Mental Calculations **Unit I0**

I3 What is 529 – 70?

Subtracting 70 is the same as subtracting I00 and adding 30.

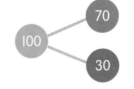

First subtract I00 from 529. 529 – 100 = 429

Then add 30 to the result. 429 + 30 = 459

529 – 70 = 459

I4 What is 936 – 80?

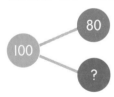

First subtract I00 from 936. 936 – (100) = (836)

Then add 20 to the result. (836) + (20) = (856)

936 – 80 = (856)

I5 Subtract mentally.

a   425 – 60 365

b   718 – 80 638

Home Maths Point out to your child that **I0** to **I2** do not involve regrouping while **I3** to **I5** do involve regrouping. Discuss how the methods differ.

I7

Teaching sequence

I3

- Revise subtraction of tens from other tens with regrouping the hundreds into tens.
- Work through the example with pupils.
  (a) Remind pupils of the number bond: 70-30—I00
  (b) Encourage pupils to recognise that subtracting 70 is the same as subtracting I00 and adding 30.
  (c) Therefore:
      529 – 100 = 429
      429 + 30 = 459

I4

- Use this question to check that pupils have understood the strategy above.
- Encourage pupils to recall the number bond: 80-20—I00

I5

- Ask pupils to subtract these numbers mentally using the strategy outlined above.

Unit I0: Mental Calculations   15

Practice 2 in Practice Book 2C,
pp 9 to 10.

Teaching sequence

- Revise subtraction of hundreds from another hundreds without regrouping.
- Show pupils the strategy to solve 827 – 400.
  (a) Remind pupils of the number bond:
      400-400—800
  (b) Subtract from left to right:
      827 – 400 = 427

- Use this question to check that pupils have understood the strategy above.
- Encourage pupils to recall the number bond: 500-200—700

- Ask pupils to subtract these numbers mentally, using the strategy above.

Unit 10 Mental Calculations

16 What is 827 – 400?

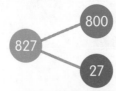

| First subtract the hundreds. | 800 – 400 = 400 |
| Then add the result to the tens and ones. | 27 + 400 = 427 |

827 – 400 = 427

17 What is 749 – 500?

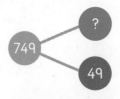

| First subtract the hundreds. | (700) – 500 = (200) |
| Then add the result to the tens and ones. | (49) + (200) = (249) |

749 – 500 = (249)

18 Subtract mentally.

    a 973 – 300 673   **b** 508 – 400 108

Practice Book 2C, p.9

18

INSPIRE MATHS

PRACTICE BOOK 2C

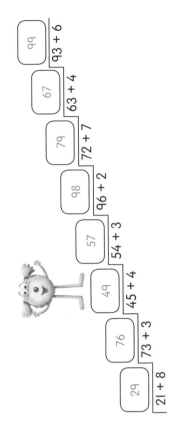

Koogol

Googol

Zoogol

Toogol

Noogol

Ooogol

Consultant and author
Dr Fong Ho Kheong

Authors
Chelvi Ramakrishnan and Michelle Choo

UK consultants
Carole Skinner, Simon d'Angelo and Elizabeth Gibbs

Unit 10 Mental Calculations

Date: _____

Practice I   Mental addition

1 Climb each step by adding the numbers mentally.
How quickly and accurately can you do them?

$$93 + 6 \quad 99$$
$$63 + 4 \quad 67$$
$$72 + 7 \quad 79$$
$$96 + 2 \quad 98$$
$$54 + 3 \quad 57$$
$$45 + 4 \quad 49$$
$$73 + 3 \quad 76$$
$$21 + 8 \quad 29$$

2 Add the numbers mentally.

a 38 + 7 = ?

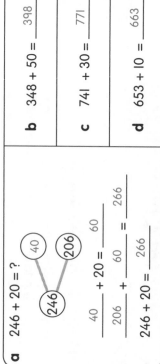

38 + 10 = 48
48 - 3 = 45
38 + 7 = 45

b 75 + 6 = ?

75 + 10 = 85
85 - 4 = 81
75 + 6 = 81

c 69 + 5 = 74

d 48 + 4 = 52

e 29 + 9 = 38

f 65 + 8 = 73

3 Match the spaceships to the astronauts.

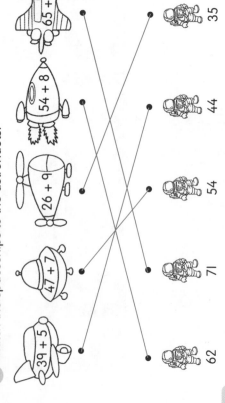

65 + 6   54 + 8   26 + 9   47 + 7   39 + 5

35   44   54   71   62

4 Add the numbers mentally.

a 123 + 5 = ?

3 + 5 = 8
120 + 8 = 128
123 + 5 = 128

b 632 + 7 = 639

c 712 + 3 = 715

d 534 + 5 = 539

f 375 + 6 = 381

g 275 + 8 = 283

h 629 + 9 = 638

e 409 + 7 = ?

409 + 10 = 419
419 - 3 = 416
409 + 7 = 416

5 Add the numbers mentally.

a 246 + 20 = ?

40 + 20 = 60
206 + 60 = 266
246 + 20 = 266

b 348 + 50 = 398

c 741 + 30 = 771

d 653 + 10 = 663

Date: _____

Practice 2 Mental subtraction

1 Subtract the numbers mentally.

a 43 − 6 = ?

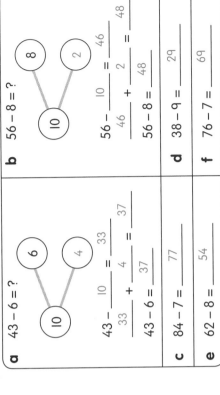

43 − 10 = $\underline{33}$

33 + 4 = $\underline{37}$

43 − 6 = $\underline{37}$

b 56 − 8 = ?

43 − 10... 56 − 10 = $\underline{46}$

46 + 2 = $\underline{48}$

56 − 8 = $\underline{48}$

c 84 − 7 = $\underline{77}$

d 38 − 9 = $\underline{29}$

e 62 − 8 = $\underline{54}$

f 76 − 7 = $\underline{69}$

2 Subtract the numbers mentally.

a 789 − 5 = ?

9 − 5 = $\underline{4}$

780 + 4 = $\underline{784}$

789 − 5 = $\underline{784}$

b 364 − 6 = ?

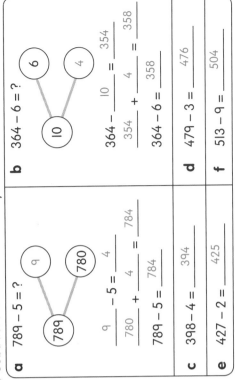

364 − 10 = $\underline{354}$

354 + 4 = $\underline{358}$

364 − 6 = $\underline{358}$

c 398 − 4 = $\underline{394}$

d 479 − 3 = $\underline{476}$

e 427 − 2 = $\underline{425}$

f 513 − 9 = $\underline{504}$

---

e 352 + 70 = ?

352 + 100 = $\underline{452}$

452 − 30 = $\underline{422}$

352 + 70 = $\underline{422}$

f 427 + 80 = $\underline{507}$

g 535 + 90 = $\underline{625}$

h 164 + 60 = $\underline{224}$

6 Add the numbers mentally.

a 315 + 200 = ?

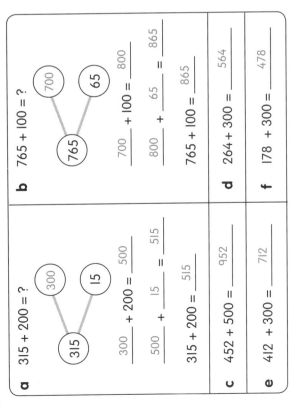

300 + 200 = $\underline{500}$

500 + 15 = $\underline{515}$

315 + 200 = $\underline{515}$

b 765 + 100 = ?

700 + 100 = $\underline{800}$

800 + 65 = $\underline{865}$

765 + 100 = $\underline{865}$

c 452 + 500 = $\underline{952}$

d 264 + 300 = $\underline{564}$

e 412 + 300 = $\underline{712}$

f 178 + 300 = $\underline{478}$

3 Subtract the numbers mentally.

a 348 – 20 = ?

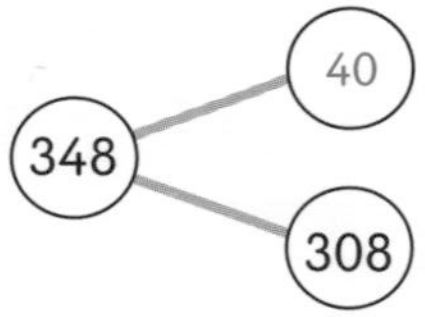

(348 → 40, 308)

40 – 20 = _20_

308 + 20 = _328_

348 – 20 = _328_

b 641 – 50 = ?

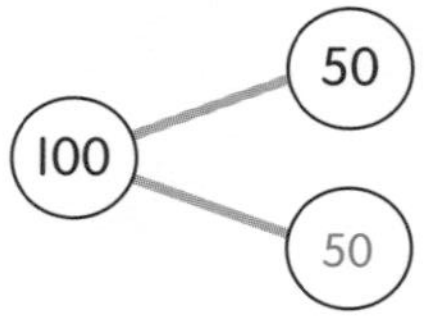

(100 → 50, 50)

641 – 100 = _541_

541 + 50 = _591_

641 – 50 = _591_

c 475 – 40 = _435_

d 516 – 70 = _446_

e 436 – 60 = _376_

f 228 – 30 = _198_

---

4 Subtract the numbers mentally.

a 256 – 100 = ?

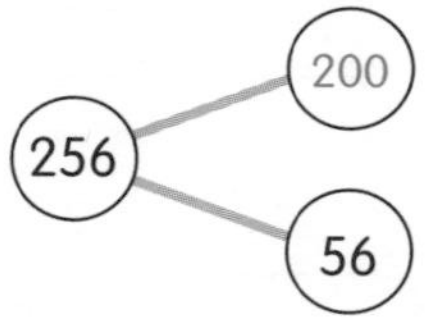

(256 → 200, 56)

200 – 100 = _100_

56 + 100 = _156_

256 – 100 = _156_

b 832 – 400 = ?

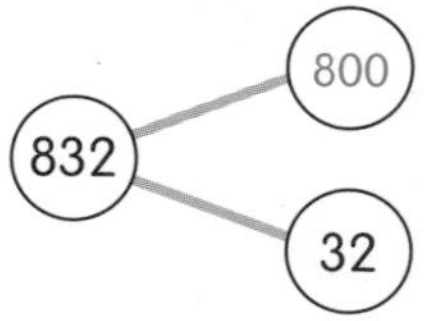

(832 → 800, 32)

800 – 400 = _400_

32 + 400 = _432_

832 – 400 = _432_

c 348 – 300 = _48_

d 548 – 300 = _248_

e 615 – 400 = _215_

f 465 – 200 = _265_

Unit 10: Mental Calculations

10

Week	Learning Objectives	Thinking Skills	Resources
2	**(I) Counting pounds and pence** Pupils will be able to: • recognise different coins and notes and know the value of each • state the total value of a set of notes and coins • write amounts of money in numbers, given the amount written in words *Let's Explore!* Pupils will be able to: • show different ways of making up a value with different notes and coins • show different ways of making up a value in pounds only, pence only or in pounds and pence	• Comparing • Identifying attributes and components • Recalling number bonds	• Pupil Textbook 2B, pp I9 to 23 • Practice Book 2C, pp II to I6 • Teacher's Guide 2B, pp 25 to 29

Week	Learning Objectives	Thinking Skills	Resources
2	**(2) Changing pounds and pence** Pupils will be able to: • convert pence to pounds • convert pence to pounds and pence • convert pounds to pence • convert pounds and pence to pence	• Comparing	• Pupil Textbook 2B, pp 24 to 25 • Practice Book 2C, pp 17 to 18 • Teacher's Guide 2B, pp 30 to 31
3	**(3) Comparing amounts of money** Pupils will be able to: • write the amount of money in a place value chart in pounds and pence • use a strategy to compare the amounts of money by first comparing the pounds followed by the pence • state the greater/greatest or smaller/smallest amount of money using the 'comparing pounds and pence' strategy	• Comparing	• Pupil Textbook 2B, pp 26 to 27 • Practice Book 2C, pp 19 to 22 • Teacher's Guide 2B, pp 32 to 33

Week	Learning Objectives	Thinking Skills	Resources
3	**(4) Word problems:** *Addition and subtraction of money* Pupils will be able to: • solve one-step or two-step word problems in addition or subtraction involving 'part-whole', 'adding on', 'taking away' or 'comparing' concepts; in pounds only or in pence only • draw models to solve word problems in pounds only or in pence only *Multiplication and division of money* Pupils will be able to: • solve one-step word problems in multiplication and division involving 'group and item' and 'multiplying' concepts • draw models to solve word problems	• Making links between addition and subtraction • Applying addition and subtraction concepts • Making links between multiplication and division	• Pupil Textbook 2B, pp 28 to 31 • Practice Book 2C, pp 23 to 26 • Teacher's Guide 2B, pp 34 to 37

Week	Learning Objectives	Thinking Skills	Resources
3	*Put On Your Thinking Caps!* Pupils will be able to use the 'making a list' method to solve a challenging problem.	• Comparing Heuristics for problem solving: • Make a list • Guess and check	• Pupil Textbook 2B, p 31 • Practice Book 2C, pp 27 to 28 • Teacher's Guide 2B, p 37
	Review 4		• Practice Book 2C, pp 29 to 36

Summative assessment opportunity

Assessment Book 2, Test 5, pp 57 to 63

Money

Counting pounds and pence

Pupils will be able to:

- recognise different coins and notes and know the value of each
- state the total value of a set of notes and coins
- write amounts of money in numbers, given the amount written in words

Key concept

The dot separates the pounds from the pence.

Thinking skills

- Comparing
- Identifying attributes and components
- Recalling number bonds

What you will need

- Play money (see Photocopy master 2 on p 250)
- Collection of notes and coins

Teaching sequence

1

- Ask pupils to work in groups.
- Carry out the following activity with pupils:
  - (a) Distribute different amounts of play money to each group.
  - (b) Ask pupils to count the values of the notes and coins separately.
  - (c) Invite volunteers to share their answers with the class, and check that their answers are correct.
  - (d) Pick a group whose answer is in pounds and pence. Encourage the class to state the value of the notes and the coins and write the answer on the board: "*Group _____ has _____ pounds and _____ pence.*" Write the amount in numbers: "£___·_____" Read the amount in words.
  - (e) Prompt pupils to explain the function of the dot.
  - (f) Invite 2 or 3 volunteers to carry out (d) with different values. Then go through the example in **1**.

Unit 11 Money

Let's Learn!

Counting pounds and pence

Jack has a £5 note and a 50p coin.

We say that he has **five pounds and fifty pence**.
We can write this as **£5·50**.

This dot is important. It separates the pence from the pounds.

19

Additional activity

Ask pupils to work in pairs.

Using the play money, give each pair two notes and two coins of different denominations.

Encourage them to count on and find the amount.

Exchange the play money with other groups and repeat the activity.

What you will need

- Play money (see Photocopy master 2 on p 250)
- Collection of notes and coins

Teaching sequence

- Ask pupils how to write in pounds only and pence only. Show pupils a £5 note and two £10 notes. Count on to get £25, then show them how to write in pounds.

- Show pupils how to read and write the total of two 10p coins and one 5p coin.
- Remind pupils to put a '0' in the pounds place when writing in pence only.
- Ensure that the decimal point is aligned with the middle of the numbers.
- Point out that notations such as **£2·5** and **£2·50p** cannot be used.

- Show pupils the 'count on' strategy to find the amount of money in pounds and pence and write down the answer.
- Guide pupils to count on and add to the amount at the same time:
  E.g. *"Start with £10.
        Add £2 to £10 to get £12."*
  Ask pupils to count out loud:
  E.g. *"10, 12, ..."*

Unit II Money

2 Miya has two £10 notes and a £5 note.

We say that she has twenty-five pounds.
We can write this amount as £25 or £25·00.

> There are no pence so we put two zeros after the dot.

3 Ella also has some money.

We say that she has twenty-five pence.
We can write this amount as 25p.
We can also write this amount as £0·25.

> There are no pounds so we put a zero before the dot.

4 Hardeep has some money.

> Let's count how much Hardeep has.

> 10 pounds, 15 pounds, 15 pounds and 50 pence, 15 pounds and 70 pence, 15 pounds and 90 pence!

20

Hardeep has fifteen pounds and ninety pence.
We can also write this amount as £15·90.

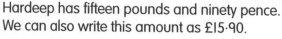

Ask pupils to work in groups.

Using the play money, give each group three notes and three coins of different denominations.

Encourage pupils to count on and find the amount.

Exchange the play money with other groups and repeat the activity.

What you will need

Play money (see Photocopy master 2 on p 250)

Money **Unit II**

5 How much does Millie have?

Write the amount of money Millie has in two different ways.

Millie has (90)p or £ (0·90).

6 How much does Peter have?

Write the amount of money Peter has in two different ways.

Peter has £ (40) or £ (40·00).

7 How much does Ruby have?

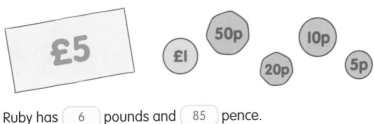

Ruby has (6) pounds and (85) pence.

She has £ (6·85).

21

Teaching sequence

- Using the strategy from ④, discuss with pupils how to count on in pence. Prompt them to write their answers in two ways:
  £_____ and _____p

- Ask pupils to work in pairs. Check pupils can use the 'count on' strategy.
- Guide pupils to write their answers as £_____·00 or £_____.

- Ask pupils to work in pairs. Check pupils can use the strategy to write the answer as £_____.

Additional activity

Ask pupils to work in groups. Ask them to list the different stationery items they could buy from a shop for £5.

Teaching sequence

 8

- Ask pupils to complete the exercise and assess their ability to count money in pounds, in pence or both.

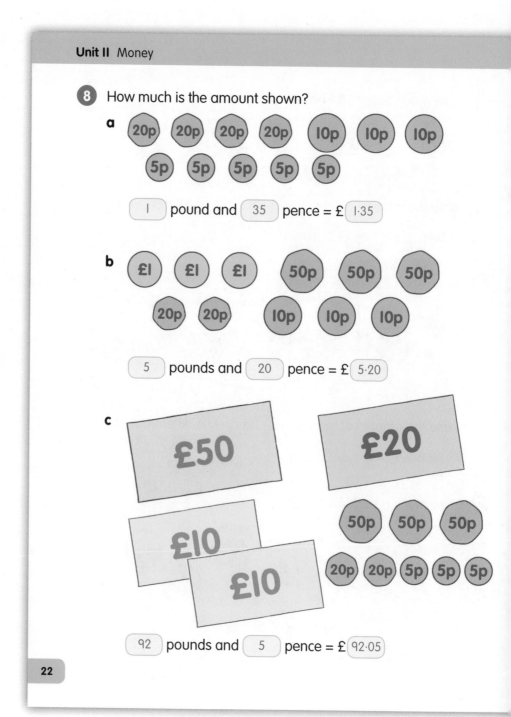

Unit II Money

8 How much is the amount shown?

a 20p 20p 20p 20p 10p 10p 10p
5p 5p 5p 5p 5p

⬚ 1 ⬚ pound and ⬚ 35 ⬚ pence = £ ⬚ 1·35 ⬚

b £1 £1 £1 50p 50p 50p
20p 20p 10p 10p 10p

⬚ 5 ⬚ pounds and ⬚ 20 ⬚ pence = £ ⬚ 5·20 ⬚

c £50 £20 £10 £10 50p 50p 50p 20p 20p 5p 5p 5p

⬚ 92 ⬚ pounds and ⬚ 5 ⬚ pence = £ ⬚ 92·05 ⬚

22

Pupils will be able to:

- show different ways of making up a value with different notes and coins
- show different ways of making up a value in pounds only, pence only or in pounds and pence

Practice I in Practice Book 2C, pp II to I6.

Money **Unit II**

Let's Explore!

9 Here are some ways you can show £10.

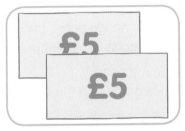

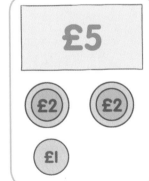

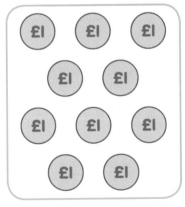

Work in groups of two or four.
Show some ways of making the following amounts.

a 90p **b** £6 **c** £5·40

> Practice Book 2C, p.II

23

Teaching sequence

9 *Let's Explore!*

- Ask pupils to work in groups.
- Ask them to write down different ways of making the amounts in **a**, **b** and **c**.

E.g. 90p

➡ Nine I0p coins

➡ Four 20p coins and one I0p coin

➡ Three 20p coins and three I0p coins

➡ One 50p coin and two 20p coins

Learning objectives: Changing pounds and pence

Pupils will be able to:

- convert pence to pounds
- convert pence to pounds and pence
- convert pounds to pence
- convert pounds and pence to pence

Key concepts

- £1 = 100p
- When changing pence to pounds, use the dot to separate the pounds from the pence.
- When changing pounds to pence, remove the dot from the pounds.

Thinking skill

Comparing

Additional activity

- Bring one hundred 1p coins or play money.
- Ask pupils to change 100p to pounds.
- Ask pupils how many pounds and how many pence there are in 100p.
- Remind pupils to put a dot after the pounds to separate the pounds from the pence.

What you will need

One hundred 1p coins or play money

Teaching sequence

- Lead pupils through the examples.
- **Note**: The examples are of different categories: less than 100p, less than 1000p and 1000p.
- Point out that the dot should be placed 2 digits from the right when changing pence to pounds.

- Lead pupils through the examples. Point out: £1 = £1·00
- To change pounds to pence, just remove the '£' sign and the dot.

- Use the question to check pupils' understanding.

Let's Learn!

Changing pounds and pence

1 We can change pence to pounds.

100p = £1·00   200p = £2·00

203p = £2·03
Two hundred and three pence is two pounds and three pence.

14p   is written as ⟹   £0·14

520p   is written as ⟹   £5·20

1000p   is written as ⟹   £10·00

2 Now change pounds to pence.
£1·50 = 150p
One pound and fifty pence is one hundred and fifty pence.

£7·95   is written as ⟹   795p

£0·08   is written as ⟹   8p

£0·50   is written as ⟹   50p

3 Answer these questions.

a   Change these to pence.

£5·00 = (500) p

£4·99 = (499) p

b   Change these to pounds.

230p = £ (2·30)

65p = £ (0·65)

24

Play money (see Photocopy master 2 on p 250)

Practice 2 in Practice Book 2C, pp 17 to 18.

- Ask pupils to work in small groups.
- Ask them to count and find out how many 50p, 20p, 10p and 5p coins there are in £1.
- Then challenge them to count and find out how many 50p coins there are in £2·50.
- Encourage the groups to use play money to show different ways of making certain amounts of money, and to write it down:
  £_____ and _____p

Money **Unit 11**

Activity

4 It's maze time!

Find out how much money each child has.
The children must keep to their colour paths.
Count on to find the total amount each child has.

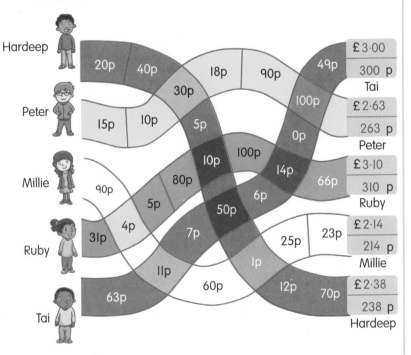

Who has the most money? Ruby

Who has the least money? Millie

Practice Book 2C, p.17

25

Teaching sequence

4

- Reinforce pupils' 'counting on' skills using this activity.
- Ask pupils to use the 'count on' strategy to find the total amounts.
- Convert the answer from pence to pounds and pence.

Pupils will be able to:

- write the amount of money in a place value chart in pounds and pence
- use a strategy to compare the amounts of money by first comparing the pounds followed by the pence
- state the greater/greatest or smaller/smallest amount of money using the 'comparing pounds and pence' strategy

Teaching sequence

- Ask pupils to place the equivalent amount of play money in pounds and pence separately.
- If necessary, align the pounds and pence values:

Pounds	Pence
29	50
32	20

This will make it easier for pupils to see which is the larger amount.

- Ask them to first compare the pounds; if the two pound values are different, then the larger amount is the one with the higher value.

- Use the same comparison method as above.
- For amounts where the pound values are the same, compare the pence to find which is the larger amount.

Key concept

Comparing amounts of money by comparing the pounds followed by the pence

Thinking skill

Comparing

Unit II Money

Let's Learn!

Comparing amounts of money

1 Who has more?

Ella has £29·50.

Pounds	Pence
29	50

Tai has £32·20.

Pounds	Pence
32	20

£32·20 is more than £29·50.
£29·50 is less than £32·20.

Tai has more money.

First compare the pounds. 32 is greater than 29.

2 Who has less?

Miya has £63·25.

Pounds	Pence
63	25

Jack has £63·70.

Pounds	Pence
63	70

£63·70 is more than £63·25.
£63·25 is less than £63·70.

Miya has less money.

First compare the pounds. They are the same.

Then compare the pence. 70 is greater than 25.

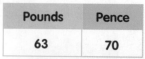

26

Additional activity

- Put different amounts of play money into 4 separate bags or envelopes.
- Ask pupils to count the money and state the different amounts in each bag or envelope.
- Challenge them to state which bag or envelope has the least/most money and arrange them in ascending order.

Money **Unit II**

Teaching sequence

3 and **4**

- Ask pupils to compare the three different amounts of money. Use the questions to assess pupils' understanding of the strategy of comparing the pounds, then the pence.

3 Millie has £20·40.
Omar has £20·25.
Peter has £20·75.

Who has the most money?
Who has the least money?

First compare the pounds. Then compare the pence.

Millie £20·40	Pounds	Pence
	20	40

Omar £20·25	Pounds	Pence
	20	25

Peter £20·75	Pounds	Pence
	20	75

£20·75 is the greatest amount.

£20·25 is the smallest amount.

Peter has the most money.

Omar has the least money.

4 Compare £40·35, £40·80 and £44·55.

Which amount is the greatest?
Which amount is the smallest?

£40·35	Pounds	Pence
	40	35

£40·80	Pounds	Pence
	40	80

£44·55	Pounds	Pence
	44	55

£44·55 is the greatest amount.

£40·35 is the smallest amount.

Arrange the amounts in order. Begin with the smallest.

£40·35, £40·80, £44·55
smallest

Practice Book 2C, p.19

27

Learning objectives: Word problems (addition and subtraction of money)

Pupils will be able to:

- solve one-step or two-step word problems in addition or subtraction involving 'part-whole', 'adding on', 'taking away' or 'comparing' concepts; in pounds only or in pence only
- draw models to solve word problems in pounds only or in pence only

Teaching sequence

- Ask pupils to read the word problem aloud.
- Explain the 'adding on' and 'taking away' concepts involved in this problem.
- Guide pupils to relate these concepts using the models in the diagram.
- Work through the addition and subtraction steps and solve the word problem.

Key concept

Solving one-step or two-step word problems involving money using addition and subtraction

Thinking skills

- Making links between addition and subtraction
- Applying addition and subtraction concepts
- Making links between multiplication and division

Unit II Money

Let's Learn!

Word problems

Addition and subtraction of money

I Ruby has £27.
Her grandmother gives her £15 more.
Then she spends £19.
How much money does Ruby have left?

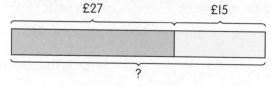

£27 + £15 = £42
Ruby has £42 altogether.

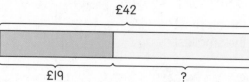

£42 − £19 = £23

Ruby has £23 left.

First find out how much money Ruby has altogether.

Home Maths
Encourage your child to compare amounts of money when you go shopping. Help them to compare prices of different brands of the same item and which is the cheapest or most expensive.

28

Teaching sequence

2

- Use the question to check pupils' understanding of two-step word problems using models.

- Encourage pupils to draw the models that show the 'adding on' and 'taking away' concepts. They should complete the exercise with the help of the models shown in the textbook.

2 Jack has £168.
Miya has £75 more than Jack.
Farha has £300.
How much more money does Farha have than Miya?

£168

Jack

£168   £75

Miya

?

 First find out how much money Miya has.

£168 + £75 = £243

Miya has £243 .

£300

Farha

£243   ?

Miya

£300 – £243 = £57

Farha has £57 more than Miya.

29

Unit II: Money **35**

Learning objectives: Word problems (multiplication and division of money)

Pupils will be able to:

- solve one-step word problems in multiplication and division involving 'group and item' and 'multiplying' concepts
- draw models to solve word problems

Key concept

Solving one-step or two-step word problems involving money using multiplication and division

Thinking skills

- Making links between multiplication and division
- Applying multiplication and division concepts

Teaching sequence

- Allow pupils to practise reading the word problems, drawing models and solving them.

- Explain the 'group and item' concept in multiplication.
- Support pupils as they draw a model, write the multiplication statement, and solve the problem.

- Explain the 'group and item' concept in division.
- Support pupils as they draw a model, write the division statement, and solve the problem.

Unit II Money

3 Answer these questions.

  a Ella has 95p.
  She has 20p less than her brother.
  How much money do Ella and her brother have altogether?

  95p + 20p = 115p
  95p + 115p = 210p = £2·10
  Ella and her brother have £2·10 altogether.

  b Miya has £450.
  She has £18 less than Hardeep.
  Hardeep spends £226 on a tent.
  How much money does he have left?

  £450 + £18 = £468
  £468 − £226 = £242
  He has £242 left.

Multiplication and division of money

4 Mrs Jones gives £3 each to her 5 children.
How much money does Mrs Jones give her children altogether?

| £3 | £3 | £3 | £3 | £3 |

5 × £3 = £15
Mrs Jones gives her children £15 altogether.

5 Peter has £32.
He puts the money equally into 4 money boxes.
How much money is there in each money box?

£32 ÷ 4 = £8

There is £8 in each money box.

30

Pupils will be able to use the 'making a list' method to solve a challenging problem.

Thinking skill
Comparing

Heuristics for problem solving
• Make a list
• Guess and check

Additional activity
• Give pupils some word problems and the correct and several incorrect answers to each.
• Ask pupils to explain which answers they think are incorrect.

Independent work
Practice 4, *Maths Journal, Challenging Practice, Problem Solving* and Review 4 in Practice Book 2C, pp 23 to 36.

Money **Unit II**

6 Answer these questions.

a Omar spends £5 each day.
How much does he spend in 6 days?
$6 \times £5 = £30$
He spends £30 in 6 days.

b Tai pays £2I for 3 T-shirts.
How much does I T-shirt cost?
$£2I \div 3 = £7$
A T-shirt costs £7.

c Ruby buys some books for £30 at a book fair.
Each book costs £5.
How many books does she buy?
$£30 \div £5 = 6$
She buys 6 books.

> Practice Book 2C, p.23

Put On Your Thinking Caps!

7 Jack saves some of his pocket money every day.
He saves his money in £2 coins and £1 coins.
At the end of the week, Jack has saved £10.
He has more than two £2 coins and more than two £1 coins.
How many £2 coins and £1 coins does he have?

Money	Quantity			
£2 coins	4	3	2	I
£1 coins	2	4	6	8
Answer	✘	✔	✘	✘

Make a list!

> Practice Book 2C, p.27   Practice Book 2C, p.28

3I

Teaching sequence

6

• Ask pupils to practise the 'group and item' concept for multiplication and division word problems.

• Remind pupils to draw models, write the mathematical statements and find the answers.

• **Note**: Use 'comparison', 'part-whole', 'adding on' and 'taking away' model drawings to help solve the problems.

7 *Put On Your Thinking Caps!*

• Encourage pupils to use the 'make a list' strategies and 'guess and check' method to find the amount of money that Jack has.

Money

Date: _____

Practice 1   Counting pounds and pence

1 Write the amount of money in numbers.

a Eighty-two pounds and seven pence

£ 82·07

b Ninety-six pence

£ 0·96

c Sixty-one pounds

£ 61·00

d Fourteen pounds and ninety-nine pence

£ 14·99

e Thirty pounds and fifty pence

£ 30·50

f Fifteen pounds

£ 15·00

g Seventy-eight pounds and twenty-five pence

£ 78·25

2 Fill in the spaces.

a £20·00 . . . . 20 pounds 0 pence

b £0·03 . . . . 0 pounds 3 pence

c £40·20 . . . . 40 pounds 20 pence

d £27·15 . . . . 27 pounds 15 pence

3 Write the amount of money in two ways.

Example

£10 or £10·00

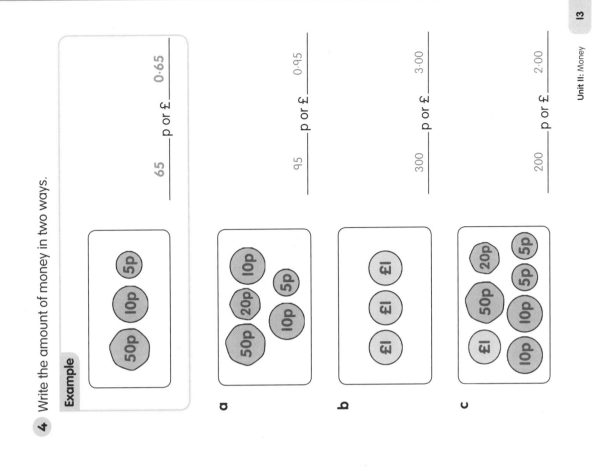

a £61 or £61·00

b £37 or £37·00

4 Write the amount of money in two ways.

Example

65 p or £ 0·65

a 95 p or £ 0·95

b 300 p or £ 3·00

c 200 p or £ 2·00

6 Match the price tags to the correct amounts of money.

£4·45

£1·03

£8·00

£13·35

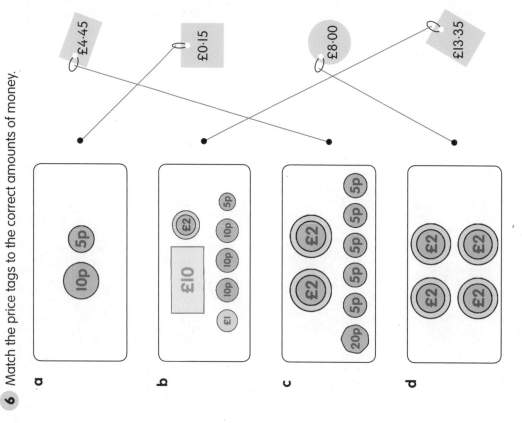

a

b

c

d

5 How much is there?

Example

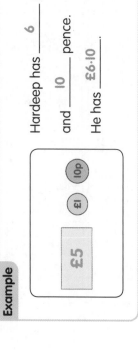

Hardeep has ___6___ pounds
and ___10___ pence.
He has ___£6·10___ .

a

Mrs Lee has ___65___ pounds
and ___50___ pence.
She has £ ___65·50___ .

b

Ruby has ___5___ pounds
and ___0___ pence.
She has £ ___5·00___ .

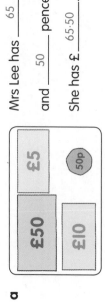

c

Tai has ___0___ pounds
and ___75___ pence.
He has £ ___0·75___ .

Practice 2 Changing pounds and pence

1 Write the amount of money in two ways.

Example

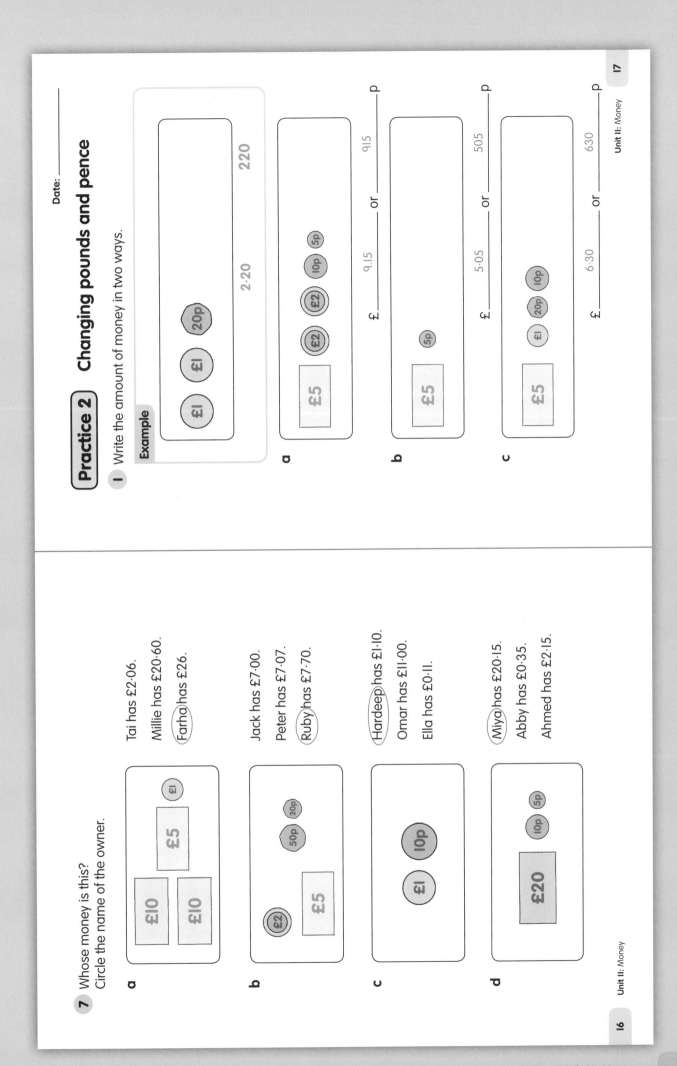

£1 £1 20p   → 2·20   220

a £5 £2 £2 10p 5p

£ _____ or _____ p
    9.15   915

b £5 5p

£ _____ or _____ p
    5·05   505

c £5 £1 20p 10p 10p

£ _____ or _____ p
    6·30   630

---

7 Whose money is this?
Circle the name of the owner.

a £10 £10 £5 £1

Tai has £2·06.
Millie has £20·60.
(Farha) has £26.

b £2 £5 50p 20p

Jack has £7·00.
Peter has £7·07.
(Ruby) has £7·70.

c £3 10p

(Hardeep) has £1·10.
Omar has £11·00.
Ella has £0·11.

d £20 10p 5p

(Miya) has £20·15.
Abby has £0·35.
Ahmed has £2·15.

Practice 3 Comparing amounts of money

1 Compare the amounts.
Complete the charts. Then fill in the spaces.

a Miya has £14·20.
Jack has £15·00.

Miya £14·20	Pounds	Pence
	14	20

Jack £15·00	Pounds	Pence
	15	00

£ _____ 15·00 _____ is more than £ _____ 14·20 _____ .

£ _____ 14·20 _____ is less than £ _____ 15·00 _____ .

Who has more money? _____ Jack _____

b Farha has £70·40.
Peter has £70·35.

Farha £70·40	Pounds	Pence
	70	40

Peter £70·35	Pounds	Pence
	70	35

£ _____ 70·40 _____ is more than £ _____ 70·35 _____ .

£ _____ 70·35 _____ is less than £ _____ 70·40 _____ .

Who has less money? _____ Peter _____

2 Write the pence in pounds.

a 20p _____ £0·20 _____   b 120p _____ £1·20 _____

c 543p _____ £5·43 _____   d 106p _____ £1·06 _____

e 350p _____ £3·50 _____   f 83p _____ £0·83 _____

g 17p _____ £0·17 _____   h 2p _____ £0·02 _____

3 Write the pounds in pence.

a £4·80 _____ 480p _____   b £3·51 _____ 351p _____

c £6·95 _____ 695p _____   d £1·05 _____ 105p _____

e £0·44 _____ 44p _____   f £0·69 _____ 69p _____

g £8 _____ 800p _____   h £7 _____ 700p _____

2 Write the amount in each space.
Then tick (✓) the box which has the greater amount.

Example

£10 £10
£10 £10
£2 £2 £2 £2 £2
_£50_ ✓

£50
£1
_£51_

a

£5 £5
10p 10p
_£10·20_ ✓

£10
5p 5p 5p
_£10·15_

b

£5
20p 20p
50p 50p
50p 50p
10p
_£7·00_

£10 £13
£2 £2
£2 £2
5p 5p 5p
_£28·15_ ✓

---

c Omar has £16·70.

Pounds	Pence
16	70

£16·70

Ruby has £16·15.

Pounds	Pence
16	15

£16·15

Ella has £16·45.

Pounds	Pence
16	45

£16·45

Do they all have the same amount of money? ___No___

£ _16·70_ is the greatest amount.

£ _16·15_ is the smallest amount.

Who has the most money? ___Omar___

Who has the least money? ___Ruby___

d Millie has £45·30.

Pounds	Pence
45	30

£ _45·30_

Hardeep has £42·95.

Pounds	Pence
42	95

£ _42·95_

Tai has £45·75.

Pounds	Pence
45	75

£ _45·75_

Who has the most money? ___Tai___

Who has the least money? ___Hardeep___

Practice 4 — Word problems

1 Hannah buys a pair of shoes for £25 and a bag for £17.
She pays with a £50 note.
How much change does she get?

£25 + £17 = £42
£50 – £42 = £8
She gets £8 change.

2 Kristina had £730.
She gave £200 to her brother.
Then her grandma gave her £250.
How much does Kristina have now?

£730 – £200 = £530
£530 + £250 = £780
Kristina has £780 now.

3 Ben had £460 in his savings account.
He saved £200 in January.
He saved another £150 in February.
How much does Ben have in his savings account now?

£460 + £200 = £660
£660 + £150 = £810
Ben has £810 in his savings now.

---

3 Circle the smaller amount.

a   (£3·85)   £4·10

b   £62·40   (£62·25)

4 Circle the greater amount.

a   (£28·90)   £27·95

b   (£71·09)   £7·90

5 Compare the amounts.

| £27·45 | £27·90 | £37·05 |

Customer A   Customer B   Customer C

a   Which customer paid the most?   Customer C

b   Which customer paid the least?   Customer A

7 Mrs Smith gives £40 to her grandchildren.
Each of them gets £5.
How many grandchildren does she have?

£40 ÷ £5 = 8
She has 8 grandchildren.

8 Mrs Baxter buys 4 bottles of shampoo.
Each bottle costs £4.
How much does she pay altogether?

4 × £4 = £16
She pays £16 altogether.

9 Alisha has £50.
She spends all her money on 5 T-shirts.
The cost of each T-shirt is the same.
How much is each T-shirt?

£50 ÷ 5 = £10
Each T-shirt is £10.

4 Mrs Brown has £600.
She pays £110 for her telephone bill and £97 for her water bill.
How much does she have left?

£600 − £110 = £490
£490 − £97 = £393
She has £393 left.

5 Emma buys some curtains for £50.
She buys some more curtains which cost £12 more.
How much does she pay altogether?

£50 + £12 = £62
£62 + £50 = £112
She pays £112 altogether.

6 Mr Anderson gives £2 to William as his pocket money every day.
What is William's pocket money in total from Monday to Friday?

£2 × 5 = £10
William's pocket money in total is £10.

Maths Journal

Date: _____

Jack has made some mistakes in his homework. Can you help him?

Example

Jack's mistake: 35p = £3·50

Correct answer: 35p = £0·35

1. Jack's mistake: One pound and sixty pence = £1·06

Correct answer: One pound and sixty pence = £1·60 or One pound and six pence = £1·06

2. Jack's mistake: 450p = £450

Correct answer: 450p = £4·50

3. Jack's mistake: £6 is £5 less than £1

Correct answer: £6 is £5 more than £1 or £6 is £5 less than £11

4. Jack's mistake: £90 is £10 more than £100

Correct answer: £90 is £10 more than £80 or £90 is £10 less than £100 or £110 is £10 more than £100

Challenging Practice

Date: _____

1. Draw the amount of money using £5, £2, 20p and 10p.

Example

£5·70

[£5] (20p)(20p) (20p)(10p)

a £4·60

Answers vary. Example:

(£2)(£2) (20p)(20p)(20p)

b £9·40

Answers vary. Example:

[£5] (£2)(£2) (20p)(10p)(10p)

Review 4

Date: _____

1. Add and subtract mentally.
   Work out the steps by joining the cards correctly.

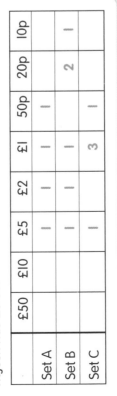

Cards (top): 84 – 6   84 + 6   64 – 8   64 + 8

Middle: Subtract 10 from 64 | Add 10 to 84 | Subtract 10 from 84 | Add 10 to 64

Next: Add 4 to the result | Add 2 to the result | Subtract 4 from the result | Subtract 2 from the result

Results: 56   90   72   78

Problem Solving

Date: _____

How many notes and coins could each person have?
Fill in the charts with 3 possible combinations for each person.

Example

Rajesh has £8·50.

	£50	£10	£5	£2	£1	50p	20p	10p
Set A			1	1	1	1		
Set B			1	1	1		2	1
Set C			1		3	1		1

1. Chantal has £60·30.

Answers vary. Example:

	£50	£10	£5	£2	£1	50p	20p	10p
Set A	1	1				1	1	1
Set B			2				1	1
Set C		6					1	1

2. Ethan has £25·00.

Answers vary. Example:

	£50	£10	£5	£2	£1	50p	20p	10p
Set A	2		1					
Set B		1	3					
Set C		1	2	2	1			

Who has the most money? _____ Chantal _____

2 Add the numbers mentally.

a 352 + 4 = 356
b 576 + 3 = 579
c 479 + 4 = 483
d 817 + 5 = 822
e 143 + 30 = 173
f 316 + 70 = 386
g 299 + 40 = 339
h 544 + 90 = 634
i 235 + 500 = 735
j 198 + 800 = 998

3 Subtract the numbers mentally.

a 916 – 5 = 911
b 876 – 4 = 872
c 873 – 8 = 865
d 375 – 9 = 366
e 587 – 30 = 557
f 477 – 60 = 417
g 354 – 80 = 274
h 146 – 90 = 56
i 794 – 200 = 594
j 858 – 400 = 458

4 Find the mystery number.
Use the clues.
Cross out the numbers on the frogs as you mentally add or subtract.

The mystery number is the one left at the end. What is it?

a It is not 7 + 26
b It is not 34 + 16
c It is not 25 + 10
d It is not 45 – 32
e It is not 19 – 8
f It is not 17 less than 31
g It is not 26 – 14
h It is not 67 more than 18
i It is not 58 – 29
j It is not 99 – 52
k It is not 16 + 11
l It is not 72 + 14

Frogs: 14, 85, 27, 86, 13, 47, 35, 50, 11, 33, 29, 12, 21

It is ___21___.

5 Ella and Omar are playing a card game.
Add or subtract mentally for each question in order.
Then for each answer, draw an 'X' on the player's card that has the number.
The first player to get three 'X' in a row wins.

a 137 + 9   = 146
b 258 + 30 = 288
c 486 – 50 = 436
d 325 + 60 = 385
e 789 – 90 = 699
f 688 – 600 = 88
g 204 – 50 = 154
h 474 + 7   = 481
i 552 + 80 = 632
j 367 – 100 = 267
k 876 – 600 = 276
l 345 + 50 = 395
m 567 + 400 = 967
n 999 – 900 = 99

Who won the game? _____ Omar

Ella

267	148	385
435	376	154
436	967	256

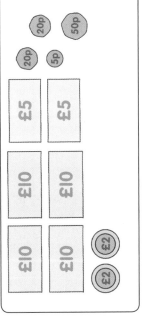

Omar

222	88	178
699	146	999
632	697	481

6 Write the amount of money in numbers.

a

| £5 | £5 | £5 |

5p 10p 10p

£10·25

b

| £10 | £10 | £5 |
| £10 | £10 | £5 |

£2 £2

20p 5p 20p 50p

£54·95

c

| £10 | £10 |
| £5 | £5 |

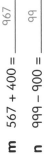

10p 10p 10p £3 £3

£32·30

7 Write the amounts in pounds or pence.

a £8·00 = __800__ p

b 325p = £ __3·25__

c £0·75 = __75__ p

d 45p = £ __0·45__

e £0·02 = __2__ p

f 6p = £ __0·06__

8 Count the amount of money in each set.
Then arrange the amounts in order, beginning with the greatest.

a

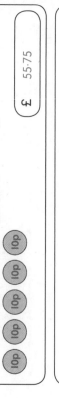

£ 13·20

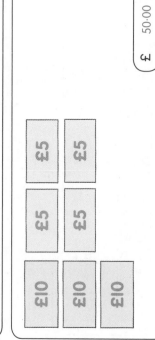

£ 13·75

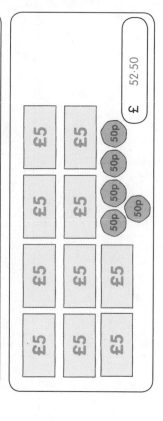

£ 13·50

__£13·75__ , __£13·50__ , __£13·20__
greatest

b

£ 55·75

£ 50·00

£ 52·50

__£55·75__ , __£52·50__ , __£50·00__
greatest

c

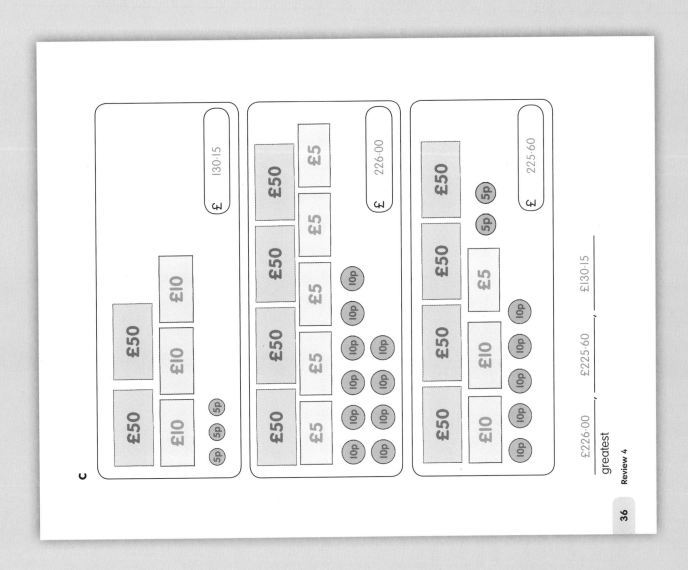

£50 £50 £10
£13 £13 £10
5p 5p 5p

£ 130·15

£50 £50 £50 £50 £50
£5 £5 £5 £5 £5
10p 10p 10p 10p 10p 10p 10p 10p 10p 10p 10p 10p

£ 226·00

£50 £50 £50 £50 £50
£10 £13 £5 5p 5p
10p 10p 10p 10p 10p 10p

£ 225·60

£226·00 , £225·60 , £130·15

greatest

Review 4

36

Week	Learning Objectives	Thinking Skills	Resources
4	**(I) Understanding fractions** Pupils will be able to: • use shapes to represent one whole and fractions with denominators of up to I2 • write fractions with denominators of up to I2 from given shapes with equal divisions • identify whether a shape has been cut into equal fractional parts • read and write fractions in words • identify parts and whole from a given situation • write fractions to represent the parts of a whole from a given situation *Let's Explore!* Pupils will be able to fold pieces of paper into equal parts in different ways.	• Analysing parts and whole • Visualising equal parts	• Pupil Textbook 2B, pp 32 to 37 • Practice Book 2C, pp 37 to 42 • Teacher's Guide 2B, pp 56 to 6I

Week	Learning Objectives	Thinking Skills	Resources
4	**(2) More fractions** Pupils will be able to: • represent fractions using model drawings • represent a situation in terms of fractions and then model drawings • represent fractions using drawings of shapes *Let's Explore!* Pupils will be able to analyse and visualise different ways in which an object can be divided equally given a fraction. *Maths Journal* Pupils will be able to recall the fraction concepts to tell a story based on model diagrams.	• Analysing and visualising parts and whole	• Pupil Textbook 2B, pp 38 to 43 • Practice Book 2C, pp 43 to 46 • Teacher's Guide 2B, pp 62 to 67

Week	Learning Objectives	Thinking Skills	Resources
5	**(3) Comparing and ordering fractions** Pupils will be able to: • compare and order two or more fractions with the same denominator using rectangular strips or model drawings of the same size • compare and order two or more fractions with different denominators using rectangular strips or model drawings of the same size • order two or more fractions with or without the use of rectangular strips of the same size or model drawings *Let's Explore!* Pupils will be able to use the 'comparing' strategy to describe which fraction is greater/smaller or the greatest/smallest.	• Comparing and contrasting two or more fractions	• Pupil Textbook 2B, pp 44 to 49 • Practice Book 2C, pp 47 to 52 • Teacher's Guide 2B, pp 68 to 73

Week	Learning Objectives	Thinking Skills	Resources
5	**(4) Adding and subtracting like fractions** Pupils will be able to: • add two or three fractions with the same denominator taken from a whole • subtract a fraction from another fraction with the same denominator taken from a whole • subtract two fractions with the same denominator from the same whole • conceptualise addition and subtraction of fractions by representing the subtraction with model drawings	• Applying parts and whole in addition and subtraction	• Pupil Textbook 2B, pp 50 to 55 • Practice Book 2C, pp 53 to 56 • Teacher's Guide 2B, pp 74 to 79
6	**(5) Solving word problems** Pupils will be able to: • recall and apply 'part-whole' and 'adding on' concepts in addition of two fractions using model drawing to solve word problems • recall and apply 'part-whole' and 'taking away' concepts in subtraction of fractions using model drawing to solve word problems	• Applying 'part-whole', 'adding on' and 'taking away' concepts in fractions • Visualising equal parts of a whole	• Pupil Textbook 2B, pp 56 to 59 • Practice Book 2C, pp 57 to 58 • Teacher's Guide 2B, pp 80 to 83
6	*Put On Your Thinking Caps!* Pupils will be able to apply the 'adding on' and 'taking away' concepts to solve model drawing problems.	• Comparing and contrasting two or more fractions	• Pupil Textbook 2B, p 59 • Practice Book 2C, pp 59 to 60 • Teacher's Guide 2B, p 83

Fractions

Learning objectives: Understanding fractions

Pupils will be able to:

- use shapes to represent one whole and fractions with denominators of up to 12
- write fractions with denominators of up to 12 from given shapes with equal divisions
- identify whether a shape has

been cut into equal fractional parts

- read and write fractions in words
- identify parts and whole from a given situation
- write fractions to represent the parts of a whole from a given situation

Key concepts

- Fractions make up equal parts of a whole. Conversely, unequal parts are not fractions of a whole.
- The symbol $\frac{1}{2}$ represents 1 out of 2 parts.
- $\frac{2}{2}$ is a whole.

Teaching sequence

- Introduce the concept of fractions by first showing a whole divided into equal parts.
- Use a square as an example which can be divided into 4 equal parts in various ways.

2

- Show pupils an example of a square that is not divided into 4 equal parts.
- Two examples are shown in the textbook.

Unit

12 **Fractions**

Let's Learn!

Understanding fractions

1 Hardeep divides a square piece of paper into 4 parts.

Each part has the same size.
We say that each part is **equal**.

He can also divide the piece of paper this way.

Can you think of another way to divide the square piece of paper into 4 equal parts?

2 This square piece of paper has not been divided into 4 equal parts

Each part does not have the same size.
We say that each part is **unequal**.

Can you think of other ways of dividing the square piece of paper into 4 unequal parts?

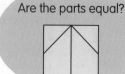
Are the parts equal?

32

Additional activity

- Ask pupils to draw a circle. Then ask them to divide it into 3 unequal parts.
- Ask pupils to draw a rectangle on a piece of paper and cut it out. Ask them to divide their rectangle into 8 equal parts in two different ways.

Fractions **Unit 12**

3 Which of these shapes have been divided into equal parts? B, C, D, E, F

A   B   C   D   E   F

4

This is a sandwich. It is one whole.

This is a cake. It is one whole too.

The pizza is divided into 2 equal parts.

If Miya eats the 2 parts, we say that she eats 2 out of 2 equal parts.

We write it as $\frac{2}{2}$.

$\frac{2}{2}$ is a whole.

If Miya eats only 1 part, we say that she eats 1 out of 2 equal parts.
We write it as $\frac{1}{2}$.

$\frac{2}{2}$ and $\frac{1}{2}$ are some examples of **fractions**.

33

Teaching sequence

- Use this question to check that pupils understand the concept of equal parts and unequal parts.
- This concept leads them to learn the concept of fractions.

- Show pupils a pizza (circle) and a sandwich (square) representing 1 whole each.
- Then using the pizza (circle), divide it into 2 equal parts to show the fraction $\frac{1}{2}$.
- Emphasise that the parts divided must be equal.
- Explain that if Miya has eaten 1 out of the 2 parts, then Miya has eaten $\frac{1}{2}$ of the pizza. The 2 parts out of the whole is $\frac{2}{2}$.
- Explain that $\frac{1}{2}$ and $\frac{2}{2}$ are fractions.

- Help pupils to divide a rectangle into 6 equal parts.
- Ask them to shade 4 equal parts.
- Encourage them to write the fraction representing the shaded parts and the unshaded parts.

Teaching sequence

- Use a similar explanation to ④ but this time using a rectangular cake (rectangle). Emphasise that the parts divided must be equal.
- Explain that if I out of the 5 parts has been eaten, then $\frac{1}{5}$ of the cake has been eaten. The 5 parts out of the whole is $\frac{5}{5}$.
- Explain that $\frac{1}{5}$ and $\frac{5}{5}$ are fractions.

- Next assess pupils using a circle divided into 4 equal parts, one of which is shaded.
- Ask pupils to write down the fraction of the shaded part.

- Assess pupils to check if they can apply this concept of fraction to solve a simple word problem.

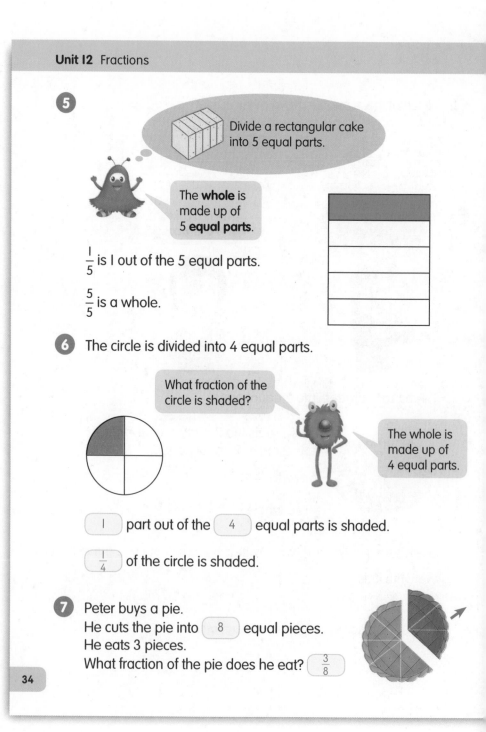

Unit 12 Fractions

⑤

Divide a rectangular cake into 5 equal parts.

The **whole** is made up of 5 **equal parts**.

$\frac{1}{5}$ is I out of the 5 equal parts.

$\frac{5}{5}$ is a whole.

⑥ The circle is divided into 4 equal parts.

What fraction of the circle is shaded?

The whole is made up of 4 equal parts.

[I] part out of the [4] equal parts is shaded.

[$\frac{1}{4}$] of the circle is shaded.

⑦ Peter buys a pie.
He cuts the pie into [8] equal pieces.
He eats 3 pieces.
What fraction of the pie does he eat? [$\frac{3}{8}$]

34

Objective of activity

Pupils will be able to fold pieces of paper into equal parts in different ways.

What you will need

- Square piece of paper
- Rectangular piece of paper
- Circular piece of paper (see Photocopy master 3 on p 251)

Let's Explore!

8 Take a square piece of paper.

1 Fold it in half.
What shape have you made?

I've made a rectangle!

I've made a triangle!

2 Fold it in half again.
What shape have you made?

I've made a square!

I've made a smaller triangle!

3 Open up the paper.
Draw lines along the folds.

I've made this!

I've made this!

How many designs can you make?

Look at these designs.
How can you make them?

Use rectangular piece of paper and a circular piece of paper.
What have you made?

35

Teaching sequence

8 *Let's Explore!*

- Ask pupils to work in pairs.
- Ask them to find different ways to fold a square piece of paper into 4 equal parts.
- Prompt pupils to follow the steps shown in the textbook.
- Ask pupils to explore different ways of folding a rectangular and a circular piece of paper into equal parts.
- Encourage them to compare their results with their friends.

Teaching sequence

- Use this activity to reinforce the fraction concepts covered earlier through paper folding.
- Pupils are expected to write answers such as, $\frac{1}{2}, \frac{1}{4}, \frac{1}{8}, \frac{3}{6}$ and $\frac{3}{12}$.

10 and **11**

- Assess whether pupils can use the concept and strategy learnt earlier to find the shaded fractional part.

What you will need

5 rectangular cut-outs of equal size (see Photocopy master 4 on p 252)

Unit 12 Fractions

Activity

9

1 Cut out five rectangles.

2 Take three rectangles and fold them in the three different ways below.
   a 2 equal parts **b** 4 equal parts **c** 8 equal parts

3 For each rectangle you have folded, shade 1 of the equal parts. What fraction of the whole is each equal part?

4 Draw lines to divide the remaining two rectangles into
   a 6 equal parts   **b** 12 equal parts

5 For each rectangle in **4a** and **4b**, shade 3 of the equal parts. What fraction of the whole is the shaded part?

10

What fraction of the circle is shaded?

$\frac{3}{4}$ of the circle is shaded.

11 What fraction of the rectangle is shaded?

36

$\frac{5}{8}$ of the rectangle is shaded.

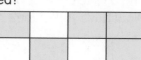

Additional activity

- Ask pupils to work in pairs.
- Ask the first pupil to write a fraction with a different numerator from those given in the textbook.

  E.g. Instead of $\frac{1}{5}$, they could write $\frac{3}{5}$.

- The second pupil reads out the fraction in words as three-fifths.

Independent work

Practice I in Practice Book 2C, pp 37 to 42.

12 How do we read fractional parts?

Fraction	Read As
$\frac{1}{2}$	one-half
$\frac{1}{3}$	one-third
$\frac{1}{4}$	one-quarter or one-fourth
$\frac{1}{5}$	one-fifth
$\frac{1}{6}$	one-sixth
$\frac{1}{7}$	one-seventh
$\frac{1}{8}$	one-eighth
$\frac{1}{9}$	one-ninth
$\frac{1}{10}$	one-tenth
$\frac{1}{11}$	one-eleventh
$\frac{1}{12}$	one-twelfth

 Home Maths Encourage your child to write and read fractional parts, based on the table above.

 Practice Book 2C, p.37

37

Teaching sequence

12

- Encourage pupils to read and write fractions in numerals and in words.
- Go through all the fractions given in the textbook in numerals and in words.
- Ask for two volunteers. Ask the first pupil to write a fraction taken from the page. Ask the second pupil to read aloud the fraction in words.
- Repeat the activity with different pairs of children.

Learning objectives: More fractions

Pupils will be able to:

- represent fractions using model drawings
- represent a situation in terms of fractions and then model drawings
- represent fractions using drawings of shapes

Key concept

Using modelling as a concept to represent fraction contexts

Thinking skill

Analysing and visualising parts and whole

Teaching sequence

- The rectangular bar is a model showing a total of 5 equal parts, of which 2 are red and 3 are yellow.
- Explain the following interpretations to pupils:
  - 5 parts in all; 2 red parts and 3 yellow parts.
  - Fraction of the whole that is yellow = $\frac{3}{5}$
  - Fraction of the whole that is red = $\frac{2}{5}$
- Emphasise that $\frac{2}{5}$ and $\frac{3}{5}$ make one whole.

Unit 12 Fractions

Let's Learn!

More fractions

Let's use models to show fractions.

The model shows a whole with 5 equal parts.

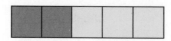

2 parts are red and 3 parts are yellow.

What fraction of the whole is red?

Number of red parts = 2

Number of parts altogether = 5

The fraction of the whole in red is $\frac{2}{5}$.

The fraction of the whole in yellow is $\frac{3}{5}$.

2 parts + 3 parts = 5 parts or I whole

$\frac{2}{5}$ and $\frac{3}{5}$ make I whole.

Additional activity

Ask pupils to work in pairs.

Pupil A draws a circle, divides it into 4 equal parts, then shades some of the parts.

Pupil B draws a bar model and shades the same number of parts as the circle.

Then they write the fractions that are represented in the models.

Pupils A and B swap roles.

The rectangle above is divided into ⟨ 5 ⟩ equal parts.

⟨ 3 ⟩ parts are shaded.

What fraction of the rectangle is shaded? ⟨ $\frac{3}{5}$ ⟩

What fraction of the rectangle is **not** shaded? ⟨ $\frac{2}{5}$ ⟩

⟨ $\frac{3}{5}$ ⟩ and ⟨ $\frac{2}{5}$ ⟩ make 1 whole.

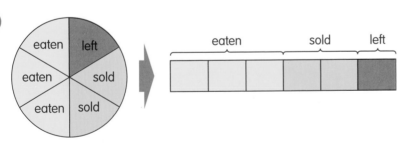

Farha's pie is cut into ⟨ 6 ⟩ equal parts.

The fraction of Farha's pie that is eaten is ⟨ $\frac{3}{6}$ ⟩.

The fraction of Farha's pie that is sold is ⟨ $\frac{2}{6}$ ⟩.

The fraction of Farha's pie that is left is ⟨ $\frac{1}{6}$ ⟩.

⟨ $\frac{3}{6}$ ⟩, ⟨ $\frac{2}{6}$ ⟩ and ⟨ $\frac{1}{6}$ ⟩ make 1 whole.

39

Teaching sequence

- The rectangular bar shows a total of 5 equal parts, of which 3 parts are shaded and 2 parts are unshaded.
- Pupils are expected to count the number of the shaded or unshaded parts and then write the fractions (instead of using subtraction to find the fraction of the unshaded part).

- A pie or a circle is used as a whole (a region model). The whole is divided in 6 equal parts and partitioned into 3 areas.
- Explain that the region model can also be shown as a rectangular bar, as in ①.

Fraction sold = $\frac{2}{6}$ (or $\frac{1}{3}$)

Fraction eaten = $\frac{3}{6}$ (or $\frac{1}{2}$)

Fraction left = $\frac{1}{6}$

- Emphasise that these 3 fractions make one whole.
- **Note**: Pupils are not required to simplify the fraction from $\frac{2}{6}$ to $\frac{1}{3}$ or $\frac{3}{6}$ to $\frac{1}{2}$ at this stage.

- Six cards, numbered I to 6 (see Photocopy master 5 on p 253)
- Bag/envelope to hold the numbered cards

Teaching sequence

- Explain to pupils that the number of pieces of oranges is 12. (This information is not given in the text.)
- Put the number cards into a bag and ask each pupil to draw out 2 cards. The first number will represent the number of pieces of orange eaten by Omar, while the second number will represent the number of pieces of orange eaten by Jack.

Example: A pupil draws the numbers 5 and 3. The following model shows the corresponding fractions:

Pieces of orange eaten by Omar = $\frac{5}{12}$.

Pieces of orange eaten by Jack = $\frac{3}{12}$.

Pieces of orange left = $\frac{4}{12}$.

Unit 12 Fractions

Activity

1. Put six number cards (I, 2, 3, 4, 5 and 6) into a bag.

2. Take two number cards from the bag.

3. The first number shows the pieces of orange that Omar ate.

4. The second number shows the remaining pieces of the same orange that Jack ate.

5. Draw a model to show the pieces Omar and Jack ate.

   What fraction of the orange did Omar eat? Answers vary

   What fraction of the orange did Jack eat? Answers vary

Activity

5 Draw these shapes.

a Draw a square with 4 equal parts.

Shade $\frac{1}{4}$ of the square.

Answers vary

b Draw a square with 6 equal parts.

Shade $\frac{1}{6}$ of the square.

c Draw a rectangle with 6 equal parts.

Shade $\frac{5}{6}$ of the rectangle.

d Draw a rectangle with 12 equal parts.

Shade $\frac{7}{12}$ of the rectangle.

e Draw a triangle with 2 equal parts.

Shade $\frac{1}{2}$ of the triangle.

f Draw a triangle with 4 equal parts.

Shade $\frac{3}{4}$ of the triangle.

41

Teaching sequence

5

• This activity helps pupils to consolidate their understanding of concepts related to fractions.

• Pupils draw shapes and shade parts to represent the fractions.

Objective of activity

Pupils will be able to analyse and visualise different ways in which an object can be divided equally given a fraction.

What you will need

Photocopy master 6 (see p 254)

Teaching sequence

6 *Let's Explore!*

- Guide pupils through this activity to gauge their analytical, visual and creative thinking skills to find different ways to divide an object into equal parts.

Unit 12 Fractions

Let's Explore!

6 Millie has a bar of chocolate.

She wants to share it with her friend.
She has thought of a way to divide the chocolate bar into 2 equal parts.

Help Millie think of four other ways to divide the chocolate bar into 2 equal parts.
Draw a model.
Show your answers by colouring the parts.

Answers vary

Example

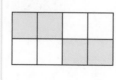

42

Objective of activity

Pupils will be able to recall the fraction concepts to tell a story based on model diagrams.

What you will need

Cubes (at least 3 different colours)

Independent work

Practice 2 in Practice Book 2C, pp 43 to 46.

Teaching sequence

7 *Maths Journal*

- Use this activity to help pupils to reflect on the fraction concepts covered so far.
- Guide pupils to recall and use concepts to tell the stories based on the model diagrams.

Maths Journal

7 Ella takes 2 yellow and 3 green ▢.
She puts them together to make a rectangular block.

$\frac{2}{5}$ of Ella's block is yellow.

$\frac{3}{5}$ of Ella's block is green.

Ella thinks of a fraction story.

> I cut a cake into 5 parts.
> I eat $\frac{2}{5}$ of the cake.
> I give away $\frac{3}{5}$ of the cake.
> I have no cake left.

I Take two different coloured 🎲.
Join them like this to make a rectangular block.

Write fraction stories about the block.

2 Make a different rectangular block with two colours.

Write fraction stories about the block.

3 Make a rectangular block with three colours.

Write fraction stories about the block.

Practice Book 2C, p.43

43

Pupils will be able to:

- compare and order two
  or more fractions with the
  same denominator using
  rectangular strips or model
  drawings of the same size

- compare and order two
  or more fractions with
  different denominators using
  rectangular strips or model
  drawings of the same size

- order two or more fractions
  with or without the use of
  rectangular strips of the same
  size or model drawings

Key concept

Quantifying and comparing
fractions

Thinking skill

Comparing and contrasting two
or more fractions

Teaching sequence

- Explain to pupils that fractions
  can be compared if they are
  taken from identical wholes.

- *Example*: These figures can be
  compared as the wholes are
  identical.

Figure A

Figure B

These figures cannot be
compared as the wholes are
not identical.

Figure C

Figure D

- In the second example,
  although visually the shaded
  area in Figure C is larger than
  the shaded area in Figure D,
  by taking the shaded area
  as a fraction of the whole,
  the shaded area in Figure D
  is actually larger than that in
  Figure C.

- In ①, the wholes are
  identical bars of the same
  length; therefore we can
  conclude visually that $\frac{5}{8}$ is
  greater than $\frac{3}{8}$ and $\frac{8}{8}$ is
  greater than $\frac{5}{8}$.

Unit I2 Fractions

Let's Learn!

Comparing and ordering fractions

① Mrs Hill has 3 cakes, all the same size.
She cuts each cake into 8 equal parts.

Jack eats $\frac{3}{8}$ of a cake, Tai eats $\frac{5}{8}$ of a cake and Miya eats $\frac{8}{8}$
of a cake.

Who eats the most?
Who eats the least?

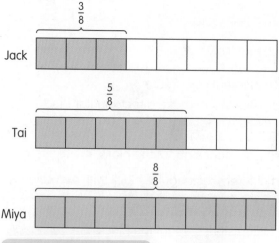

$\frac{5}{8}$ is greater than $\frac{3}{8}$.
Tai eats more than
Jack.

$\frac{8}{8}$ is greater than $\frac{5}{8}$.
Miya eats more
than Tai.

$\frac{3}{8}$ is smaller than $\frac{5}{8}$ and $\frac{8}{8}$.
Jack eats less than
Tai and Miya.

Miya eats the most.
Jack eats the least.

44

---

68   **Unit I2:** Fractions

2 Farha buys two pizzas, both the same size.

Peter eats $\frac{2}{5}$ of a pizza and Hardeep eats $\frac{4}{5}$ of the other pizza.

Who eats less?

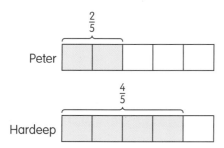

Peter

Hardeep

$\frac{2}{5}$ is smaller than $\frac{4}{5}$.
Peter eats less.

3 Millie bakes two chicken pies, both the same size.
She cuts each pie into 6 equal parts.

Tai eats $\frac{3}{6}$ of a pie and Omar eats $\frac{2}{6}$ of the other pie.

Who eats more?

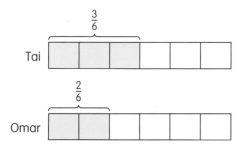

Tai

Omar

($\frac{3}{6}$) is greater than ($\frac{2}{6}$).

(Tai) eats more.

45

2

- Using a similar explanation as in **1**, show that $\frac{2}{5}$ is smaller than $\frac{4}{5}$.
- Ask pupils to compare fractions with the same denominator using models.
- Show pupils that for fractions with the same denominator, comparing the numerator will show which fraction is smaller or greater.

3

- Assess pupils informally to check whether they have understood the concept and strategy for comparing two fractions using the strategy given in **1** and **2**.

Ask pupils to work in pairs.

Pupil A writes down three fractions with the same denominator (less than or equal to 12).

Pupil B draws and shades model parts to show these fractions.

Encourage pupils to arrange the fractions from the smallest to the greatest.

Teaching sequence

- Explain to pupils that for a comparison of more than two fractions, the above strategy still holds. For fractions with the same denominator, comparing the numerator they can tell which fractions are the smallest or the greatest.

- Use the question to check whether pupils understand the concept and strategy for comparing three fractions using the strategy given in ❶ and ❷.

Unit 12 Fractions

④ Arrange the fractions in order. Begin with the greatest.

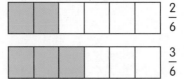

$\dfrac{3}{6}$ is the greatest.

$\dfrac{1}{6}$ is the smallest.

$\dfrac{3}{6}$, $\dfrac{2}{6}$, $\dfrac{1}{6}$
greatest

⑤ Arrange the fractions in order. Begin with the smallest.

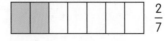

$\boxed{\dfrac{5}{7}}$ is the greatest.

$\boxed{\dfrac{2}{7}}$ is the smallest.

$\boxed{\dfrac{2}{7}}$, $\boxed{\dfrac{3}{7}}$, $\boxed{\dfrac{5}{7}}$
smallest

46

6 Jack eats $\frac{1}{2}$ of a cake.

Hardeep eats $\frac{1}{4}$ of the **same** cake.

Who eats more?

 Jack

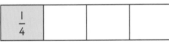 Hardeep

$\frac{1}{2}$ is greater than $\frac{1}{4}$.
Jack eats more.

7 Ruby eats $\frac{1}{4}$ of a chocolate bar.

Omar eats $\frac{1}{3}$ of the **same** chocolate bar.

Who eats less?

 Ruby

 Omar

$\frac{1}{4}$ is smaller than $\frac{1}{3}$.
Ruby eats less.

8 Below are two rectangles of the same size.
Which fraction is greater?
Which fraction is smaller?

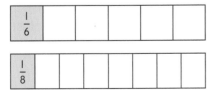

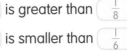 is greater than .

$\frac{1}{8}$ is smaller than $\frac{1}{6}$.

47

Teaching sequence

- Explain to pupils that in the previous questions, we compared two or more fractions with the same denominator. Here, the two fractions have different denominators but they are drawn from the same whole.

- Use this strategy to compare the two fractions.

   (a) Draw two identical models.

   (b) Divide the first model into 2 equal parts and shade $\frac{1}{2}$.
   Divide the second model into 4 equal parts and shade $\frac{1}{4}$.

   (c) Compare the two fractions to see that $\frac{1}{2}$ is greater than $\frac{1}{4}$.

- Using the same method, compare $\frac{1}{4}$ and $\frac{1}{3}$.

- Use this question to check pupils' understanding of the strategy above.

Ask pupils to draw and arrange fraction strips with the numerator I and denominators from 2 to I2. Ask them to compare the different strips and confirm that for fractions with the same numerator, the greater the denominator, the smaller the fraction will be.

Teaching sequence

9 and **10**

- Guide pupils to use the same strategy for four fractions with different denominators and the same numerator, to arrange them in order.
- Point out to pupils the following patterns for fractions with the same numerator.
  - The greater the denominator, the smaller the fraction will be.
  - The converse is true: the smaller the denominator, the greater the fraction will be.

11 and **12**

- Ask pupils to practise using this strategy to answer these questions.

Unit I2 Fractions

9 Arrange the fractions in order, beginning with the smallest.

$\dfrac{1}{7}$, $\dfrac{1}{6}$, $\dfrac{1}{3}$, $\dfrac{1}{2}$
smallest

10 Arrange the fractions in order, beginning with the greatest.

$\dfrac{1}{5}$, $\dfrac{1}{7}$, $\dfrac{1}{9}$, $\dfrac{1}{12}$
greatest

11 Arrange the fractions in order, beginning with the smallest.

a $\dfrac{10}{10}$, $\dfrac{7}{10}$, $\dfrac{2}{10}$, $\dfrac{6}{10}$ $\frac{2}{10}, \frac{6}{10}, \frac{7}{10}, \frac{10}{10}$ b $\dfrac{1}{10}$, $\dfrac{1}{8}$, $\dfrac{1}{11}$, $\dfrac{1}{5}$ $\frac{1}{11}, \frac{1}{10}, \frac{1}{8}, \frac{1}{5}$

12 Arrange the fractions in order, beginning with the greatest.

a $\dfrac{3}{12}$, $\dfrac{11}{12}$, $\dfrac{5}{12}$, $\dfrac{8}{12}$ $\frac{11}{12}, \frac{8}{12}, \frac{5}{12}, \frac{3}{12}$ b $\dfrac{1}{12}$, $\dfrac{1}{3}$, $\dfrac{1}{9}$, $\dfrac{1}{4}$ $\frac{1}{3}, \frac{1}{4}, \frac{1}{9}, \frac{1}{12}$

48

In the *Let's Explore* activity, pupils will be able to use the 'comparing' strategy to describe which fraction is greater/smaller or the greatest/smallest.

What you will need

- 8 paper strips of equal length for each group (see Photocopy master 7 on p 255)
- Glue
- A large piece of plain paper (big enough to stick all of the fraction strips on)

Independent work

Practice 3 in Practice Book 2C, pp 47 to 52.

Let's Explore!

13 You will need eight paper strips of the same size.

1 Take one strip and label it like this:

> one whole

2 Fold a second strip into 2 equal parts.
Then unfold the strip and draw a line along the fold.
Write $\frac{1}{2}$ on one part of the strip.

3 Now make these parts with the remaining strips.

$$\frac{1}{3}, \frac{1}{4}, \frac{1}{6}, \frac{1}{8}, \frac{1}{10}, \frac{1}{12}$$

4 Colour the named parts. Arrange the strips in order, beginning with the longest coloured part. Stick them onto a large piece of paper.

one whole		
$\frac{1}{2}$		
$\frac{1}{3}$		
$\frac{1}{4}$		

5 a Which fraction is the greatest?

b Which fraction is the smallest?

c Name a fraction which is greater than $\frac{1}{6}$.

d Name a fraction which is smaller than $\frac{1}{8}$.

Maths Journal

14 Look at the fractions and the lengths of the coloured parts.
Do you see a pattern?
Write what you see.

> Practice Book 2C, p.47

49

Teaching sequence

13 *Let's Explore!*

- Guide pupils to divide the strips into equal sections and then arrange them in ascending or descending order.
- Point out to pupils that:
  - Starting with $\frac{1}{2}$, they can make $\frac{1}{4}$ and $\frac{1}{8}$ by folding the strip of paper in half each time.
  - Starting with $\frac{1}{3}$, they can make $\frac{1}{6}$ and $\frac{1}{12}$ by folding the strip of paper in half each time.

14 *Maths Journal*

- Guide pupils to see that the smaller the denominator, the greater the fraction and vice versa.
- Point out that this is only true if the fractions have the same numerator.

Pupils will be able to:

- add two or three fractions with the same denominator taken from a whole

- subtract a fraction from another fraction with the same denominator taken from a whole

- subtract two fractions with the same denominator from the same whole

- conceptualise addition and subtraction of fractions by representing the subtraction with model drawings

Key concept

Quantifying, adding and subtracting fractions

Thinking skill

Applying parts and whole in addition and subtraction

Teaching sequence

- Point out to pupils that fractions can be added like whole numbers when they are quantified.

- Use concrete representation to show that $\frac{1}{5}$ and $\frac{3}{5}$ can be added when presented in pictorial form or using bar models.

- Show pupils that for fractions with the same denominators, the numerators can be added like whole numbers.

   E.g. To add $\frac{1}{5}$ and $\frac{3}{5}$, we add

   the numerators:

   $1 + 3 = 4$

   The result is $\frac{4}{5}$.

Unit 12 Fractions

Let's Learn!

Adding and subtracting like fractions

1 Ella eats $\frac{1}{5}$ of a pizza.

Tai eats $\frac{3}{5}$ of it.

What fraction of the pizza do they eat altogether?

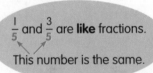
$\frac{1}{5}$ and $\frac{3}{5}$ are **like** fractions.
This number is the same.

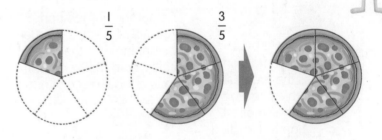

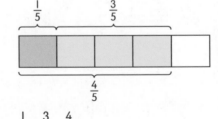

$\frac{1}{5} + \frac{3}{5}$
= 1 fifth + 3 fifths
= 4 fifths

$\frac{1}{5} + \frac{3}{5} = \frac{4}{5}$

They eat $\frac{4}{5}$ of the pizza altogether.

50

Additional activity

Ask pupils to give two fractions with the same denominator (less than or equal to 12).

Then ask pupils to draw a bar model and shade parts of the bar to show the two fractions and the addition of them.

Teaching sequence

2 and **3**

- Use these questions to check pupils' understanding of the models representing the addition of two fractions.

4

- Use this question to check pupils' understanding of the model representing the addition of three fractions.

2 Add $\frac{3}{8}$ and $\frac{4}{8}$.

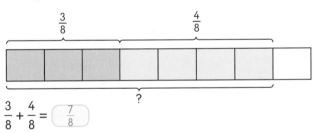

$\frac{3}{8} + \frac{4}{8} = \boxed{\frac{7}{8}}$

3 What is $\frac{2}{9} + \frac{3}{9}$?

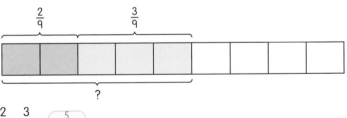

$\frac{2}{9} + \frac{3}{9} = \boxed{\frac{5}{9}}$

4 What is $\frac{1}{7} + \frac{2}{7} + \frac{4}{7}$?

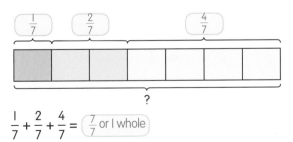

$\frac{1}{7} + \frac{2}{7} + \frac{4}{7} = \boxed{\frac{7}{7} \text{ or I whole}}$

51

Additional activity

Draw a rectangular bar model with 12 equal divisions on the board.

Shade some parts red and some parts blue.

Encourage pupils to write an addition story and a subtraction story based on this model.

Teaching sequence

- Point out to pupils that fractions can be subtracted like whole numbers when they are quantified.
- Use concrete representation to show that $\frac{2}{7}$ can be subtracted from $\frac{6}{7}$ when presented in pictorial form or using bar models.
- Show pupils that for fractions with the same denominator, the numerators can be subtracted like whole numbers.

  E.g. To subtract $\frac{2}{7}$ from $\frac{6}{7}$, we subtract the numerators:

  $6 - 2 = 4$

  The result is $\frac{4}{7}$.

- Use this question to check pupils' understanding of the model representing two fractions and subtracting them.

Unit 12 Fractions

5 Millie reads $\frac{2}{7}$ of a book before dinner.

She continues reading after dinner.

She reads $\frac{6}{7}$ of the book altogether.

What fraction of the book does Millie read after dinner?

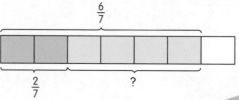

$\frac{6}{7} - \frac{2}{7} = \frac{4}{7}$

Millie reads $\frac{4}{7}$ of the book after dinner.

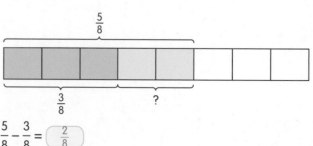

$\frac{6}{7} - \frac{2}{7}$
= 6 sevenths – 2 sevenths
= 4 sevenths

6 Subtract $\frac{3}{8}$ from $\frac{5}{8}$.

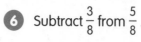

$\frac{5}{8} - \frac{3}{8} = \boxed{\frac{2}{8}}$

7 What is $\frac{7}{9} - \frac{2}{9}$?

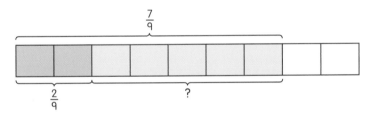

$\frac{7}{9} - \frac{2}{9} = \boxed{\frac{5}{9}}$

8 What is $1 - \frac{3}{5}$?

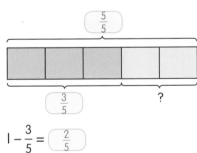

I whole $= \frac{5}{5}$

$1 - \frac{3}{5} = \boxed{\frac{2}{5}}$

9 Answer these questions.

a $\frac{3}{7} + \frac{2}{7}$ $\frac{5}{7}$

b $\frac{4}{9} + \frac{2}{9}$ $\frac{6}{9}$

c $\frac{6}{11} + \frac{5}{11}$ $\frac{11}{11}$ or I whole

d $\frac{1}{12} + \frac{3}{12} + \frac{5}{12}$ $\frac{9}{12}$

e $\frac{7}{8} - \frac{4}{8}$ $\frac{3}{8}$

f $\frac{9}{10} - \frac{3}{10}$ $\frac{6}{10}$

g $1 - \frac{7}{12}$ $\frac{5}{12}$

h $1 - \frac{1}{6} - \frac{3}{6}$ $\frac{2}{6}$

53

Teaching sequence

7
- Use this question to check pupils' understanding of the model representing two fractions and subtracting them.

8
- Use this question to check pupils' understanding of the model and subtract the fraction from a whole.

9
- Encourage pupils to practise addition and subtraction of fractions with like denominators to consolidate their understanding of the strategy.

- Fractional pieces of a circle
  (see Photocopy master 8 on
  pp 256 to 257)
- Bag/envelope to hold all the
  pieces

Teaching sequence

⑩ *Game*

- Use this game to consolidate
  pupils' understanding of
  the 'part-whole' concept in
  addition and subtraction of
  fractions.
- Point out to pupils addition of
  fractions that make one whole
  and those that do not.

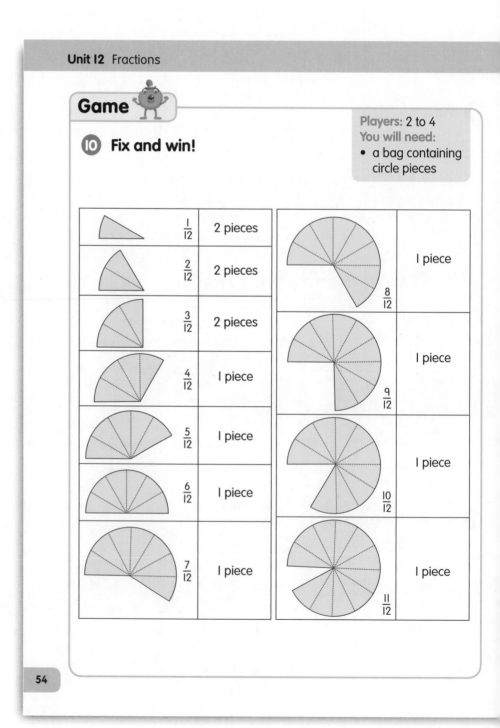

Unit 12 Fractions

Game

⑩ Fix and win!

Players: 2 to 4
You will need:
- a bag containing
  circle pieces

	$\frac{1}{12}$	2 pieces
	$\frac{2}{12}$	2 pieces
	$\frac{3}{12}$	2 pieces
	$\frac{4}{12}$	1 piece
	$\frac{5}{12}$	1 piece
	$\frac{6}{12}$	1 piece
	$\frac{7}{12}$	1 piece

	$\frac{8}{12}$	1 piece
	$\frac{9}{12}$	1 piece
	$\frac{10}{12}$	1 piece
	$\frac{11}{12}$	1 piece

54

Game

How to play:

1   Player 1 takes a circle piece from the bag and puts it on the table.

2   Player 2 takes another circle piece and joins this to the first piece on the table. If it makes more than a whole, put the second piece back into the bag.

3   Take turns to take a circle piece from the bag.

The first player to complete the circle wins!

Practice Book 2C, p.53

55

Learning objectives: Solving word problems

Pupils will be able to:

- recall and apply 'part-whole' and 'adding on' concepts in addition of two fractions using model drawing to solve word problems
- recall and apply 'part-whole' and 'taking away' concepts in subtraction of fractions using model drawing to solve word problems

Key concept

Applying the 'adding on', 'taking away', 'part-whole' and comparing concepts in solving word problems involving fractions

Thinking skills

- Applying 'part-whole', 'adding on' and 'taking away' concepts in fractions
- Visualising equal parts of a whole

Teaching sequence

- Use concrete representation to show the 'taking away' concept in subtraction.
- Encourage pupils to say:
  "I have 4 parts in a whole. I take away $\frac{1}{4}$ which is one part, and I have $\frac{3}{4}$ left."
  "I have 4 parts in a whole. I take away $\frac{3}{4}$ which is 3 parts, and I have $\frac{1}{4}$ left."

- Use this question to assess pupils' understanding.

Unit 12 Fractions

Let's Learn!

Solving word problems

1. Googol divides a pie into 4 equal parts.

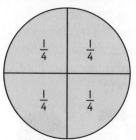

Each part is $\frac{1}{4}$.

Googol eats $\frac{1}{4}$ of the pie.

$\frac{3}{4}$ of the pie is left.

2. Farha divides a pie into 8 equal parts. She eats 3 pieces of the pie.

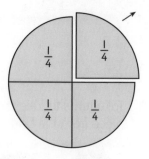

$\boxed{\frac{3}{8}}$ of the pie is eaten.

$\boxed{\frac{5}{8}}$ of the pie is left.

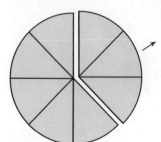

56

3 Jack has a puzzle with 6 equal parts.
He drops the puzzle and wants to put the pieces together.

 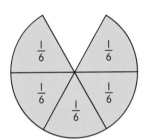

He puts together $\frac{5}{6}$ of the puzzle.

He needs another $\frac{1}{6}$ to make the whole puzzle.

4 Googol wants to make a circle with 8 equal parts.

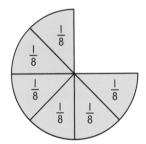

He makes $\boxed{\frac{6}{8}}$ of the circle.

He needs $\boxed{\frac{2}{8}}$ of the circle to make 1 whole.

57

- Guide pupils through the example in **3** and check their understanding of the concept using **4**.

Additional activity
Prompt pupils to think of other things that can be divided into equal parts, and to tell a subtraction story involving the fractions.

Teaching sequence

- Relate this question to the 'part-whole' concept and point out the similarities between fractions and whole numbers for 'part-whole' subtraction.

6 and **7**

- Note that **6** is a 'part-whole' addition problem and **7** is a 'part-whole' subtraction problem.
- Encourage pupils to draw models to help them solve the problems.

Unit 12 Fractions

5 Mrs Lewis gives $\frac{7}{12}$ of a pizza to Ruby.

Ruby gives some of her pizza to Jack and has $\frac{3}{12}$ of the pizza left. What fraction of the pizza does Jack get?

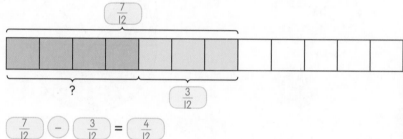

$\boxed{\frac{7}{12}} \boxed{-} \boxed{\frac{3}{12}} = \boxed{\frac{4}{12}}$

Jack gets $\boxed{\frac{4}{12}}$ of the pizza.

6 $\frac{3}{8}$ of a class have fish as pets.

Another $\frac{1}{8}$ of the class have hamsters as pets.

The rest of the class do not have any pets.

What fraction of the class have fish and hamsters as pets?

$\boxed{\frac{3}{8}} \boxed{+} \boxed{\frac{1}{8}} = \boxed{\frac{4}{8}}$

$\boxed{\frac{4}{8}}$ of the class have fish and hamsters as pets.

7 Millie eats $\frac{2}{9}$ of a packet of sweets in the morning.

She continues eating the packet of sweets in the evening.

She eats $\frac{8}{9}$ of the packet of sweets altogether.

What fraction of the packet of sweets does Millie eat in the evening?

$\boxed{\frac{8}{9}} \boxed{-} \boxed{\frac{2}{9}} = \boxed{\frac{6}{9}}$

Millie eats $\boxed{\frac{6}{9}}$ of the packet of sweets in the evening.

58

Objectives of activity

Pupils will be able to apply the 'adding on' and 'taking away' concepts to solve model drawing problems.

Thinking skill

Comparing and contrasting two or more fractions

Independent work

Challenging Practice and *Problem Solving* in Practice Book 2C, pp 59 to 60.

Fractions **Unit 12**

8 Ruby draws a picture.

She colours $\frac{4}{12}$ of the picture in red and $\frac{5}{12}$ in blue.

She does not colour the rest of the picture.

What fraction of the picture does Ruby colour?

$$\left(\frac{4}{12}\right) + \left(\frac{5}{12}\right) = \left(\frac{9}{12}\right)$$

Ruby colours $\left(\frac{9}{12}\right)$ of the picture.

Practice Book 2C, p.57

Put On Your Thinking Caps!

9 Look at the model below.
What fraction must be added to it to make 1 whole? $\frac{7}{12}$

$\frac{5}{12}$

Now look at the model below.
What fraction must be added to it to make $\frac{3}{4}$? $\frac{4}{12}$

$\frac{5}{12}$?

$\frac{3}{4}$

Practice Book 2C, p.59

Practice Book 2C, p.60

59

Teaching sequence

8

- Note that this is a 'part-whole' addition problem.

9 *Put On Your Thinking Caps!*

- Pupils are expected to interpret the model to solve the question.

Unit 12: Fractions   **83**

Fractions

Unit 12

Date: _____

Practice 1   Understanding fractions

1 Put a tick (✓) in the box if the shape is divided into equal parts.

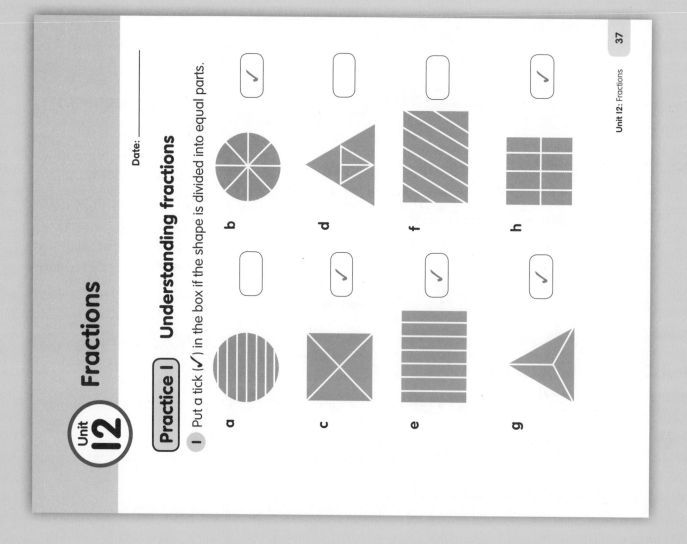

a [ ]

b [✓]

c [✓]

d [ ]

e [✓]

f [ ]

g [✓]

h [✓]

4 Cross (**X**) the odd ones out.

a

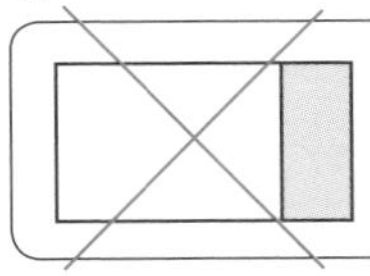

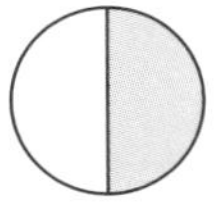

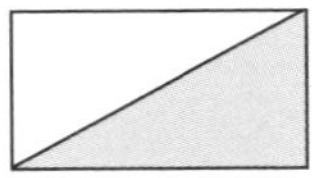

one-half

b one-quarter

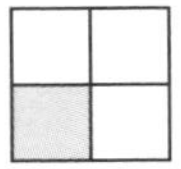

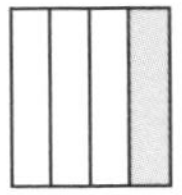

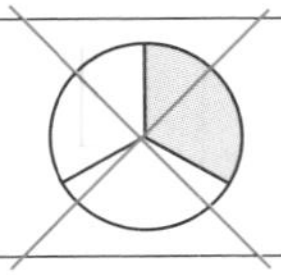

c

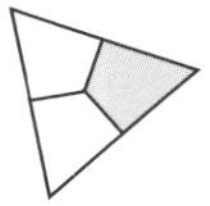

one-third

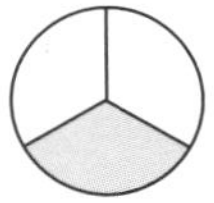

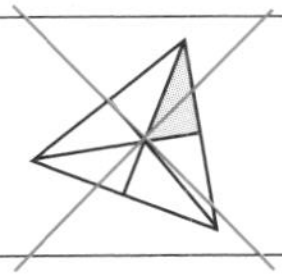

d one-sixth

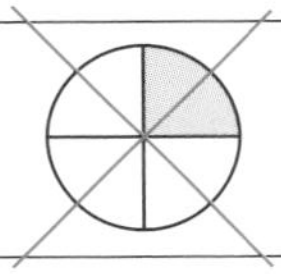

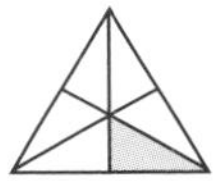

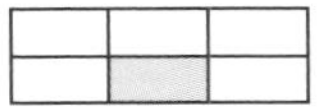

e

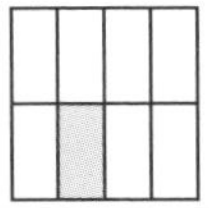

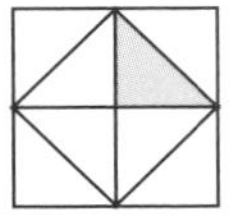

one-eighth

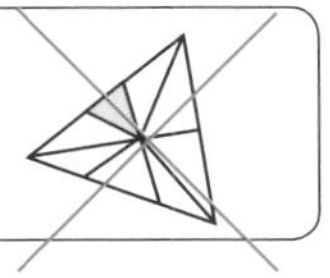

---

2 Look at the pictures carefully.
Then fill in the boxes.

a

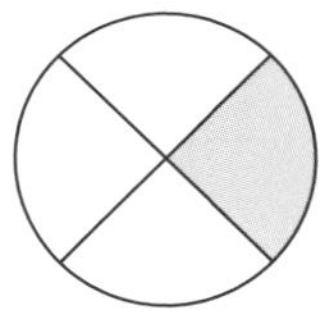

The circle is divided into

$\boxed{4}$ equal parts.

$\boxed{\dfrac{1}{4}}$ of the circle is shaded.

b

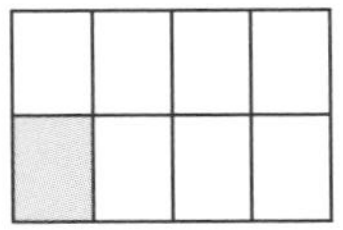

The rectangle is divided into

$\boxed{8}$ equal parts.

$\boxed{\dfrac{1}{8}}$ of the rectangle is shaded.

3 What fraction is shaded?
Circle the answers.

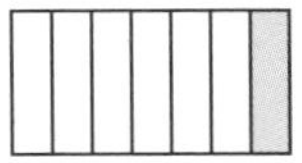 $\dfrac{1}{6}$	one-seventh	one-sixth	$\dfrac{1}{7}$
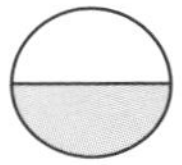 one-half	one-twos	$\dfrac{1}{2}$	1
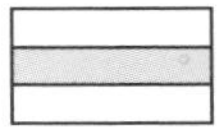 $\dfrac{1}{2}$	$\dfrac{1}{3}$	one-third	one-threes

5 Fill in the spaces.

Example

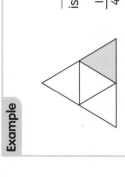

____1____ out of ____4____ equal parts is shaded.

$\frac{1}{4}$ of the shape is shaded.

a

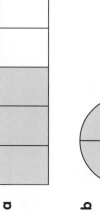

____3____ out of ____8____ equal parts are shaded.

$\frac{3}{8}$ of the shape is shaded.

b

____5____ out of ____6____ equal parts are shaded.

$\frac{5}{6}$ of the shape is shaded.

c

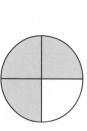

____5____ out of ____8____ equal parts are shaded.

$\frac{5}{8}$ of the shape is shaded.

6 Part of each shape is shaded.
What fraction of each shape is shaded?
Write the fraction in the box.

a

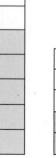

$\frac{3}{5}$

b

$\frac{3}{4}$

c

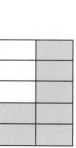

$\frac{5}{8}$

d

$\frac{7}{10}$

e

$\frac{4}{9}$

Practice 2 More fractions

1. What fraction of each shape is **not** shaded? Match the fractions to the shapes.

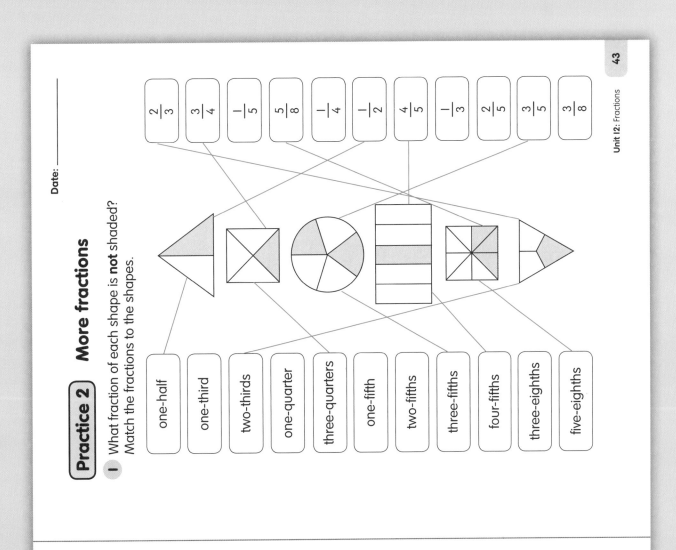

$\frac{2}{3}$ $\frac{3}{4}$ $\frac{1}{5}$ $\frac{5}{8}$ $\frac{1}{4}$ $\frac{1}{2}$ $\frac{4}{5}$ $\frac{1}{3}$ $\frac{2}{5}$ $\frac{3}{5}$ $\frac{3}{8}$

one-half
one-third
two-thirds
one-quarter
three-quarters
one-fifth
two-fifths
three-fifths
four-fifths
three-eighths
five-eighths

7. Shade part(s) of each shape to show the fraction given.

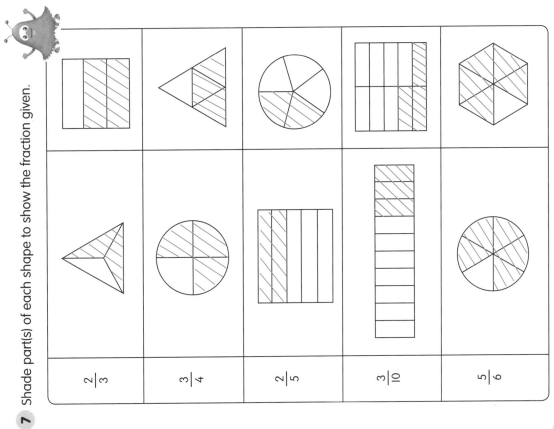

$\frac{2}{3}$

$\frac{3}{4}$

$\frac{2}{5}$

$\frac{3}{10}$

$\frac{5}{6}$

2

Each shape has been divided into equal parts.
Shade 2 or more parts of each shape.
Then fill in the spaces. Answers vary

Example

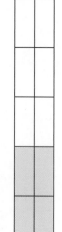

$\underline{3}$ parts out of $\underline{4}$ equal parts are shaded.

$\frac{3}{4}$ of the shape is shaded.

$\frac{1}{4}$ of the shape is not shaded.

a

_____ parts out of _____ equal parts are shaded.

_____ of the shape is shaded.

_____ of the shape is not shaded.

b

_____ parts out of _____ equal parts are shaded.

_____ of the shape is shaded.

_____ of the shape is not shaded.

c

_____ parts out of _____ equal parts are shaded.

_____ of the shape is shaded.

_____ of the shape is not shaded.

3

A chocolate bar has 10 equal parts.
Peter eats 4 parts.

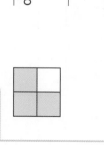

a $\underline{6}$ parts are left.

b The fraction of the chocolate eaten by Peter is $\frac{4}{10}$ or $\frac{2}{5}$.

c The fraction of the chocolate left is $\frac{6}{10}$ or $\frac{3}{5}$.

d $\frac{4}{10}$ and $\frac{6}{10}$ make 1 whole.

or $\frac{2}{5}$ and $\frac{3}{5}$ make 1 whole.

4

Miya wants to make a train with 10 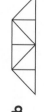 .
She joins 7 together.

a She adds $\underline{3}$ more to complete the train.

b What fraction of the cubes are grey? $\frac{7}{10}$

c What fraction of the cubes are white? $\frac{3}{10}$

d $\frac{3}{10}$ and $\frac{7}{10}$ make 1 whole.

Practice 3 Comparing and ordering fractions

1 Omar cut 3 rectangular cakes into 9 equal parts each.
Omar ate $\frac{5}{9}$ of a cake.
Millie ate $\frac{4}{9}$ of a cake and Ruby ate $\frac{8}{9}$ of a cake.
Colour to show the amount of cake eaten by each child.

Omar $\frac{5}{9}$

Millie $\frac{4}{9}$

Ruby $\frac{8}{9}$

$\frac{5}{9}$ is greater than ___$\frac{4}{9}$___.

Omar ate more than ___Millie___.

___$\frac{8}{9}$___ is greater than $\frac{5}{9}$.

___Ruby___ ate the most.

___Millie___ ate the least.

2 a What fraction of each shape is shaded?
Circle the greater fraction.

$\left(\frac{4}{5}\right)$

$\frac{2}{5}$

b Fill in the spaces with the fractions above.

$\frac{2}{5}$ is smaller than ___$\frac{4}{5}$___.

5 Tai is doing a 12-piece puzzle but some pieces are missing.

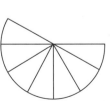

puzzle   missing pieces

a ___5___ pieces are missing.

b ___7___ pieces are in place.

c What fraction of the puzzle is missing? ___$\frac{5}{12}$___

d What fraction of the puzzle does Tai have? ___$\frac{7}{12}$___

e ___$\frac{5}{12}$___ and ___$\frac{7}{12}$___ make 1 whole.

6 Find the fractions.

a ___$\frac{3}{10}$___ and ___$\frac{7}{10}$___ make 1 whole.

b ___$\frac{4}{9}$___ and ___$\frac{5}{9}$___ make 1 whole.

c ___$\frac{6}{12}$___ and ___$\frac{6}{12}$___ make 1 whole.

d ___$\frac{3}{11}$___ and ___$\frac{8}{11}$___ make 1 whole.

6 Circle the greatest fraction.

a			b		
$\frac{3}{10}$	$\frac{1}{10}$	$\left(\frac{9}{10}\right)$	$\frac{2}{9}$	$\left(\frac{7}{9}\right)$	$\frac{5}{9}$

7 Circle the smallest fraction.

a			b		
$\frac{5}{7}$	$\left(\frac{1}{7}\right)$	$\frac{2}{7}$	$\frac{9}{11}$	$\left(\frac{5}{11}\right)$	$\frac{7}{11}$

8 Arrange each set of fractions in order.

a Begin with the greatest.

$$\frac{3}{8}, \frac{7}{8}, \frac{5}{8}$$

$\frac{7}{8}$, $\frac{5}{8}$, $\frac{3}{8}$

greatest

b Begin with the smallest.

$$\frac{8}{10}, \frac{4}{10}, \frac{7}{10}$$

$\frac{4}{10}$, $\frac{7}{10}$, $\frac{8}{10}$

smallest

---

3 Circle the smaller fraction.

a		b	
$\frac{4}{5}$	$\left(\frac{2}{5}\right)$	$\left(\frac{1}{8}\right)$	$\frac{5}{8}$

4 Circle the greater fraction.

a		b	
$\frac{3}{7}$	$\left(\frac{5}{7}\right)$	$\frac{5}{11}$	$\left(\frac{10}{11}\right)$

5 a Circle the greatest fraction.

$\frac{2}{8}$ $\left(\frac{6}{8}\right)$ $\frac{3}{8}$

b Circle the smallest fraction.

$\frac{5}{6}$ $\frac{4}{6}$ $\left(\frac{3}{6}\right)$

Page 50

9 Circle the greater fraction.

a  $\dfrac{1}{3}$ (circled) $\dfrac{1}{4}$

b 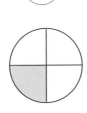 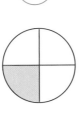  $\dfrac{1}{4}$ (circled)

10 Circle the smaller fraction.

a  $\dfrac{1}{5}$ $\dfrac{1}{6}$ (circled)

b 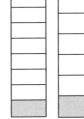 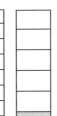 $\dfrac{1}{8}$ (circled) $\dfrac{1}{6}$

11 Circle the greater fraction.

a $\dfrac{1}{10}$, $\boxed{\dfrac{1}{8}}$ (circled)

b $\boxed{\dfrac{1}{5}}$ (circled), $\dfrac{1}{7}$

Page 51

12 Circle the smaller fraction.

a $\dfrac{1}{2}$, $\boxed{\dfrac{1}{5}}$ (circled)

b $\boxed{\dfrac{1}{9}}$ (circled), $\dfrac{1}{6}$

13 Hardeep is given sets of fractions.
Help him to arrange the fractions in order.

$\left(\dfrac{1}{6} \quad \dfrac{1}{4} \quad \dfrac{1}{5}\right)$

$\left(\dfrac{1}{7} \quad \dfrac{1}{12} \quad \dfrac{1}{8}\right)$

$\left(\dfrac{1}{9} \quad \dfrac{1}{5} \quad \dfrac{1}{11}\right)$

a Begin with the greatest.

$\dfrac{1}{4}$, $\dfrac{1}{5}$, $\dfrac{1}{6}$

greatest

b Begin with the smallest.

$\dfrac{1}{12}$, $\dfrac{1}{8}$, $\dfrac{1}{7}$

smallest

c Begin with the greatest.

$\dfrac{1}{5}$, $\dfrac{1}{9}$, $\dfrac{1}{11}$

greatest

Practice 4

Adding and subtracting like fractions

1 Write the correct fraction in each box.

a

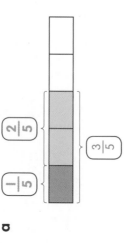

$\frac{1}{5}$ $\frac{2}{5}$

$\frac{3}{5}$

$\frac{1}{5} + \frac{2}{5} = \frac{3}{5}$

b

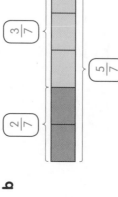

$\frac{2}{7}$ $\frac{3}{7}$

$\frac{5}{7}$

$\frac{2}{7} + \frac{3}{7} = \frac{5}{7}$

c

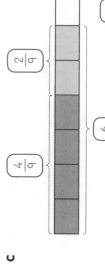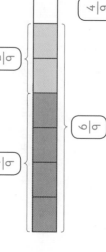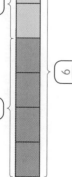

$\frac{4}{9}$ $\frac{2}{9}$

$\frac{6}{9}$

$\frac{4}{9} + \frac{2}{9} = \frac{6}{9}$

14 Colour the strips to show the fractions.
Then fill in the spaces using these fractions.

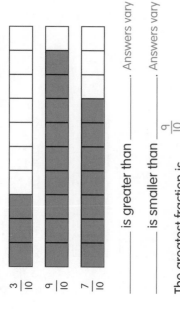

$\frac{3}{10}$

$\frac{9}{10}$

$\frac{7}{10}$

_____ is greater than _____. Answers vary

_____ is smaller than _____. Answers vary

The greatest fraction is $\frac{9}{10}$.

The smallest fraction is $\frac{3}{10}$.

15 Colour the strips to show the fractions.
Then fill in the spaces using these fractions.

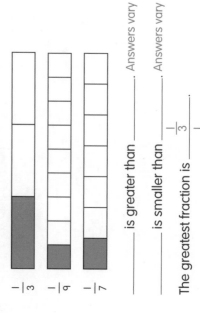

$\frac{1}{3}$

$\frac{1}{9}$

$\frac{1}{7}$

_____ is greater than _____. Answers vary

_____ is smaller than _____. Answers vary

The greatest fraction is $\frac{1}{3}$.

The smallest fraction is $\frac{1}{9}$.

3 Add these fractions.

a) $\dfrac{1}{4} + \dfrac{2}{4} = \dfrac{3}{4}$

b) $\dfrac{1}{3} + \dfrac{1}{3} = \dfrac{2}{3}$

c) $\dfrac{2}{5} + \dfrac{2}{5} = \dfrac{4}{5}$

d) $\dfrac{3}{7} + \dfrac{1}{7} = \dfrac{4}{7}$

e) $\dfrac{2}{9} + \dfrac{5}{9} = \dfrac{7}{9}$

f) $\dfrac{5}{11} + \dfrac{4}{11} = \dfrac{9}{11}$

g) $\dfrac{1}{2} + \dfrac{1}{2} = \dfrac{2}{2}$ or 1 whole

h) $\dfrac{1}{4} + \dfrac{3}{4} = \dfrac{4}{4}$ or 1 whole

i) $\dfrac{1}{6} + \dfrac{3}{6} = \dfrac{4}{6}$

j) $\dfrac{3}{9} + \dfrac{1}{9} = \dfrac{4}{9}$

k) $\dfrac{2}{10} + \dfrac{3}{10} + \dfrac{4}{10} = \dfrac{9}{10}$

l) $\dfrac{5}{12} + \dfrac{4}{12} + \dfrac{2}{12} = \dfrac{11}{12}$

2 Write the correct fraction in each box.

a)

$\dfrac{2}{6}$ $\dfrac{3}{6}$ $\dfrac{5}{6}$

$\dfrac{5}{6} - \dfrac{2}{6} = \dfrac{3}{6}$ or $\dfrac{1}{2}$

b)

$\dfrac{1}{7}$ $\dfrac{5}{7}$ $\dfrac{6}{7}$

$\dfrac{6}{7} - \dfrac{1}{7} = \dfrac{5}{7}$

c)

$\dfrac{5}{9}$ $\dfrac{2}{9}$ $\dfrac{7}{9}$

$\dfrac{7}{9} - \dfrac{5}{9} = \dfrac{2}{9}$

Date: _____

Practice 5   Solving word problems

Fill in the spaces. Use the circles to help you.

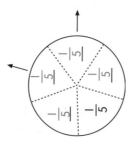

Example

Ella divides a biscuit into 4 equal parts.

Each part is $\dfrac{1}{4}$.

Ella eats $\dfrac{3}{4}$ of the biscuit.

$\boxed{\dfrac{4}{4}} - \boxed{\dfrac{3}{4}} = \boxed{\dfrac{1}{4}}$

$\dfrac{1}{4}$ —— of the biscuit is left.

1 Farha cuts a circle into 5 equal parts.

She removes $\dfrac{2}{5}$ of the circle.

$\boxed{\dfrac{5}{5}} - \boxed{\dfrac{2}{5}} = \boxed{\dfrac{3}{5}}$

$\dfrac{3}{5}$ —— of the circle is left.

2 Tai cuts a pizza into 6 equal pieces.
He gives 4 pieces away.
What fraction of the pizza is left?

$\boxed{\dfrac{6}{6}} - \boxed{\dfrac{4}{6}} = \boxed{\dfrac{2}{6}}$

$\dfrac{2}{6}$ —— of the pizza is left.

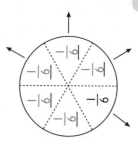

---

4 Subtract these fractions.

a $\dfrac{4}{5} - \dfrac{2}{5} = \dfrac{2}{5}$

b $\dfrac{5}{6} - \dfrac{4}{6} = \dfrac{1}{6}$

c $\dfrac{8}{9} - \dfrac{4}{9} = \dfrac{4}{9}$

d $\dfrac{9}{11} - \dfrac{3}{11} = \dfrac{6}{11}$

e $\dfrac{6}{7} - \dfrac{3}{7} = \dfrac{3}{7}$

f $\dfrac{11}{12} - \dfrac{4}{12} = \dfrac{7}{12}$

g $\dfrac{5}{6} - \dfrac{1}{6} = \dfrac{4}{6}$

h $\dfrac{7}{8} - \dfrac{3}{8} = \dfrac{4}{8}$

i $1 - \dfrac{7}{9} = \dfrac{2}{9}$

j $1 - \dfrac{5}{10} = \dfrac{5}{10}$

k $\dfrac{8}{12} - \dfrac{2}{12} = \dfrac{5}{12}$

l $\dfrac{9}{12} - \dfrac{1}{12} - \dfrac{3}{12} = \dfrac{5}{12}$

Challenging Practice

1 Colour the strips to show the fractions.

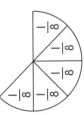

$\frac{1}{2}$

$\frac{1}{3}$

$\frac{1}{4}$

Arrange the fractions in order, beginning with the smallest.

$\frac{1}{4}$, $\frac{1}{3}$, $\frac{1}{2}$

_____ , _____ , _____
smallest

2 Draw diagrams to compare these fractions.

$\frac{1}{6}$, $\frac{1}{8}$, $\frac{1}{10}$

$\frac{1}{6}$

$\frac{1}{8}$

$\frac{1}{10}$

Then arrange the fractions in order, beginning with the greatest.

$\frac{1}{6}$, $\frac{1}{8}$, $\frac{1}{10}$

_____ , _____ , _____
greatest

---

3 Ella divides a pie into 8 equal pieces.
She gives away some pieces of pie.
She has $\frac{5}{8}$ of the pie left.

What fraction of the pie does she give away?

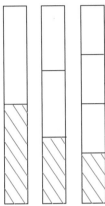

$\boxed{\frac{8}{8}} - \boxed{\frac{5}{8}} = \boxed{\frac{3}{8}}$

She gives away $\frac{3}{8}$ of the pie.

4 Peter baked a round loaf of bread.
He cut the bread into 6 equal pieces.
He ate some pieces.

$\frac{2}{6}$ of the bread was left.

$\boxed{\frac{6}{6}} - \boxed{\frac{2}{6}} = \boxed{\frac{4}{6}}$

Peter ate $\frac{4}{6}$ of the bread.

5 A circle has been divided into 10 equal pieces.
Millie joins 6 of the pieces together as shown.
What fraction of the circle does she need
to make a whole?

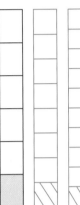

$\boxed{\frac{10}{10}} - \boxed{\frac{6}{10}} = \boxed{\frac{4}{10}}$

She needs $\frac{4}{10}$ of the circle to make a whole.

Date: _____

Problem Solving

1 A special balloon holds a prize.
Find the balloon by crossing out all the fractions greater than $\frac{1}{8}$.
The remaining one is the special balloon!

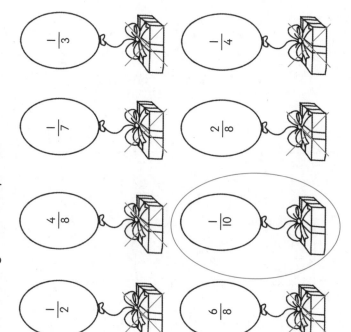

Week	Learning Objectives	Thinking Skills	Resources
6	**(1) The minute hand** Pupils will be able to: • recite the 5 times table and relate it to the clock's minute markings • recall and use the conversion: 60 minutes = 1h • tell the time as ___ mins after ___ o'clock • read and write the time in minutes to intervals of 5 minutes • name the numeral or draw the minute hand given the time in hours and minutes	• Recall the 5 times table and relate it to the minute hand	• Pupil Textbook 2B, pp 60 to 63 • Practice Book 2C, pp 61 to 64 • Teacher's Guide 2B, pp 100 to 103
6	**(2) Reading and writing the time** Pupils will be able to: • tell the time in hours and minutes by looking at the positions of the hour and minute hands • write the time in hours and minutes in numerals • draw the position of the hour hand or the minute hand given the time in numerals • make up stories about what they were doing at the times shown	• Analysing positions of hour and minute hands	• Pupil Textbook 2B, pp 64 to 68 • Practice Book 2C, pp 65 to 68 • Teacher's Guide 2B, pp 104 to 108

Week	Learning Objectives	Thinking Skills	Resources
7	**(3) Learning a.m. and p.m.** Pupils will be able to: • write times in a.m. or p.m. to differentiate between morning, afternoon and evening • choose a.m. or p.m. based on clues such as 'in the morning', 'afternoon', 'evening' or 'night' • arrange a sequence of events in order, beginning with the earliest *Maths Journal* Pupils will be able to reinforce their understanding of time and events and relate time with events.	• Analysing events and relating to a.m. or p.m. • Recalling and relating	• Pupil Textbook 2B, pp 69 to 73 • Practice Book 2C, pp 69 to 70 • Teacher's Guide 2B, pp I09 to II3
7	**(4) Time taken in hours and minutes** Pupils will be able to: • find the duration in terms of I hour or half an hour given start and end times • find the start time given the end time and duration of I hour or half an hour • find the end time given the start time and duration of I hour or half an hour	• Analysing time and event	• Pupil Textbook 2B, pp 74 to 77 • Practice Book 2C, pp 7I to 77 • Teacher's Guide 2B, pp II4 to II7

Medium-term plan

Week	Learning Objectives	Thinking Skills	Resources
7	*Put on Your Thinking Caps!* Pupils will be able to: • tell the correct time for a clock that is running slow • tell the correct time for a clock that is running fast	• Analysing time and event	• Pupil Textbook 2B, p 78 • Practice Book 2C, pp 78 to 80 • Teacher's Guide 2B, p 118
	Review 5		• Practice Book 2C, pp 81 to 88

Summative assessment opportunities

Assessment Book 2, Test 6, pp 65 to 70
For extension, Assessment Book 2, Challenging Problems 3, pp 71 to 72
Assessment Book 2, Check-up 3, pp 73 to 82

Time

Learning objectives:
The minute hand

Pupils will be able to:

- recite the 5 times table and relate it to the clock's minute markings

- recall and use the conversion: 60 minutes = 1 h

- tell the time as __ min after __ o'clock

- read and write the time in minutes to intervals of 5 minutes

- name the numeral or draw the minute hand given the time in hours and minutes

Key concepts

- The minute is a unit of measurement for time.

- The minute hand of the clock is used to indicate the time in minutes.

Thinking skill

Recall the 5 times table and relate it to the minute hand

Teaching sequence

 1

- Ask pupils to recite the 5 times table.

- Show pupils the clock face and point out that each numeral represents the time in minutes in multiples of 5.

- Ask pupils to say:
"5, 10, 15, ..., 55."
Then encourage pupils to read the time:
"10 five, 10 ten, 10 fifteen, ..., 10 fifty-five, 11 o'clock."

- Point out to pupils that we do not use 60 mins as that tells the hour, and that 60 mins = 1 h.

- Give pupils practice using the clock. Prompt them to tell the time as you change the position of the minute hand.

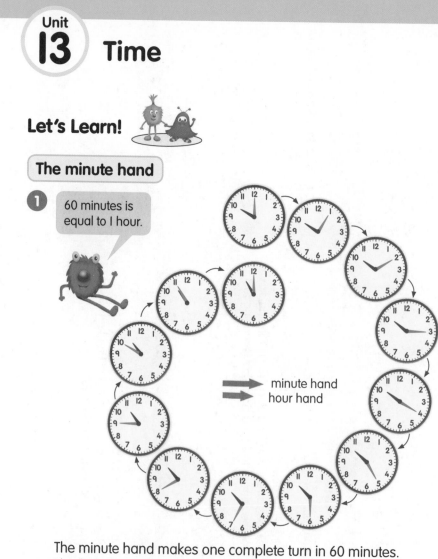

Unit 13 Time

Let's Learn!

The minute hand

1 60 minutes is equal to 1 hour.

minute hand
hour hand

The minute hand makes one complete turn in 60 minutes.
The hour hand moves from 10 to 11 in 1 hour.

 Home Maths Look at a clock together at different times of day. Encourage your child to look at the minute hand and say how many minutes it shows.

60

What you will need

A big clock face with only the minute hand (see Photocopy master 9 on p 258)

Objective of activity

Pupils will be able to associate the number on the clock with the corresponding number of minutes.

2

8 o'clock

5 minutes later →

5 minutes past 8 o'clock

3

8 o'clock

40 minutes later →

We count in fives. 5, 10, 15, 20, 25, 30, 35, 40.

40 minutes past 8 o'clock

4

8 o'clock

20 minutes later →

20 minutes past 8 o'clock

61

Teaching sequence

• Move the minute hand to point to I. Prompt pupils to recognise and read as "*Five minutes past 8 o'clock.*"

• Make sure pupils are able to read the number I on the clock as 5 minutes.

• Starting from 8 o'clock, move the minute hand to point to 8. Encourage pupils to read the number 8 on the clock as 40 minutes.

• Guide pupils to count on by 5: "*5, 10, 15, ..., 40.*"

• Check whether pupils can read the number 4 as 20 minutes. Emphasise the use of the 'counting by 5' strategy used in and .

Ask pupils to work in pairs.

Pupil A shows a time on the clock.

Pupil B tells the time using the words 'past' and 'before'.

A big clock face (see Photocopy master 9 on p 258)

Teaching sequence

5

- Use this question to check pupils' understanding. Discuss the number 9 as 45 minutes. Emphasise the use of the 'counting by 5' strategy used in **2** and **3**.

6

- Use this question to check pupils' understanding. Discuss the number 3 as 15 minutes, and the number 10 as 50 minutes. Emphasise the use of the 'counting by 5' strategy used in **2** and **3**.

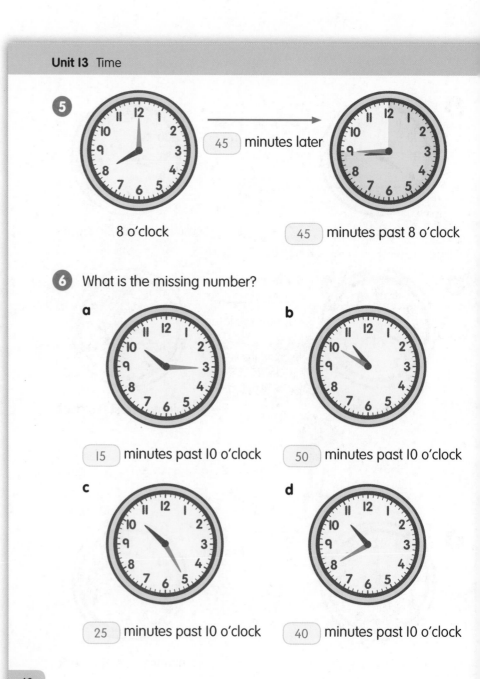

Unit 13 Time

5

45 minutes later

8 o'clock   45 minutes past 8 o'clock

6 What is the missing number?

a   b

15 minutes past 10 o'clock   50 minutes past 10 o'clock

c   d

25 minutes past 10 o'clock   40 minutes past 10 o'clock

62

Practice I in Practice Book 2C,
pp 6I to 64.

Time **Unit I3**

Activity

7 Work in pairs.

Use the clock face below to do this activity.

I Your partner calls out the minutes.

2 You point to the correct number on the clock face.

3 Take turns.

50 minutes.

Practice Book 2C, p.6I

63

Teaching sequence

7

- Guide pupils as they carry out the activity to reinforce the skills and strategy outlined earlier.

Learning objectives: Reading and writing the time

Pupils will be able to:

- tell the time in hours and minutes by looking at the positions of the hour and minute hands
- write the time in hours and minutes in numerals
- draw the position of the hour hand or the minute hand given the time in numerals
- make up stories about what they were doing at the times shown

Teaching sequence

- Encourage pupils to recognise times in word and numeral form, and to associate given times with specific daily events, e.g., going to school.
- Show the written and numeral forms of time:
  E.g. Eight twenty = 8:20
        Eight fifty = 8:50
- Challenge pupils to write the time as they read. Write '9:25' and 'Nine twenty-five' on the board and read it out loud.

Key concept

Hours and minutes are measures of time.

Thinking skill

Analysing positions of hour and minute hands

What you will need

A clock face with minute and hour hands (see Photocopy master 9 on p 258)

Additional activity

Ask pupils what time they wake up and what time they leave home for school. Give pupils the opportunity to say the time and show it on the clock face.

Teaching sequence

- Work through the examples of telling the time in the textbook.

Oh dear!
It's **eight forty-five**.
The bus is not here yet!

We write eight forty-five as 8:45.

My school bus will come at **eight thirty-five**.

We write eight thirty-five as 8:35.

65

Additional activity

Ask pupils to work in pairs.

Pupil A shows a time on the clock.

Pupil B writes and tells the time in words and in numerals.

What you will need

A big clock face (see Photocopy master 9 on p 258)

Teaching sequence

- Check whether pupils can link the time shown on the clock and the written form of the time.
- Pupils should be able to recognise, read and write the time in numerals. Check to make sure that they do not confuse the hour hand with the minute hand.

Unit 13 Time

2 Read and write the time.

As the minute hand moves, here's how we read the time.

a

It is 3:05.

b

It is 3:15.

c

It is 3:25.

d

It is 3:30.

e

It is 3:45.

f

It is 3:55.

66

3 Where should the missing hands be to show the correct time?

9:25

Draw the missing minute hand, hour hand, or both!

a 4:45

b 3:30

c 2:15

d 12:10

e 10:50

f 6:25

g 1:40

h 8:20

i 5:35

67

- Check whether pupils can link the time shown on the clock and the written form of the time.
- Ask pupils to draw the correct missing hand on the clock, given the other hand and the time.

Ask pupils to work in pairs.

Pupil A calls out a time, e.g., seven forty-five.

Pupil B shows the time on the clock.

Pupils A and B swap roles.

What you will need

A big clock face (see Photocopy master 9 on p 258)

Additional activity

Ask pupils to work in pairs.

Pupil A tells a story; e.g., "Jack is having dinner with his parents."

Pupil B says a time when this activity could be carried out; e.g., 7 o'clock.

Pupils A and B swap roles.

Practice 2 in Practice Book 2C, pp 65 to 68.

Teaching sequence

- Challenge pupils to tell the time shown and then make up stories for these times. E.g. 'At 9:25, I have a snack.'

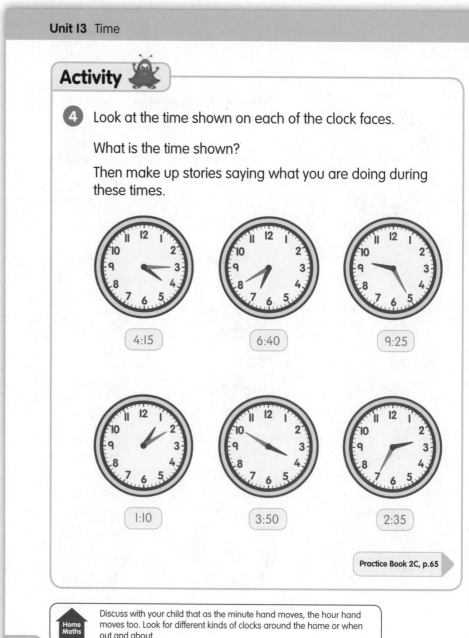

Unit 13 Time

Activity

4 Look at the time shown on each of the clock faces.

What is the time shown?

Then make up stories saying what you are doing during these times.

| 4:15 | 6:40 | 9:25 |

| 1:10 | 3:50 | 2:35 |

Practice Book 2C, p.65

Home Maths Discuss with your child that as the minute hand moves, the hour hand moves too. Look for different kinds of clocks around the home or when out and about.

68

Pupils will be able to:

- write times in a.m. or p.m. to differentiate between morning, afternoon and evening
- choose a.m. or p.m. based on clues such as 'in the morning', 'afternoon', 'evening' or 'night'
- arrange a sequence of events in order, beginning with the earliest

Key concepts

- Time is told in a.m. and p.m.
- 'a.m.' is used for time after 12 midnight to just before 12 noon.
- 'p.m.' is used for time after 12 noon to just before 12 midnight.

Thinking skills

- Analysing events and relating to a.m. or p.m.
- Recalling and relating

What you will need

A clock with minute and hour hands (see Photocopy master 9 on p 258)

Time **Unit 13**

Let's Learn!

Learning a.m. and p.m.

1 Miya wants to go to the cinema.

The film starts at **twelve fifteen** in the afternoon or **12:15 p.m.**

> We use p.m. to talk about time just after noon to just before midnight.

She has to leave the house earlier than that time.

She leaves the house at **eleven forty** in the morning or **11:40 a.m.**

> We use a.m. to talk about time just after midnight to just before noon.

69

Teaching sequence

1

- Use the following scenario to introduce the notation for before noon and after noon:
  - (a) Show 5 o'clock on a clock.
  - (b) Ask pupils what they would be doing at 5 o'clock in the morning and 5 o'clock in the afternoon.
  - (c) When discussing the activities done in the morning, write the time on the board and write 'a.m.' next to it. Point out that 'a.m.' is used for times just after 12 midnight to just before 12 noon.
  - (d) When discussing the activities done in the afternoon, write the time on the board and write 'p.m.' next to it. Point out that 'p.m.' is used for times just after 12 noon to just before 12 midnight.
- Work through the examples in the textbook and show pupils how time is written in words and in numeral form with a.m. and p.m. notation.

- Show the time 3:10 on the clock and ask a volunteer to write the time on the board.
- Describe something that pupils will do in the afternoon and ask them to guess whether the time is 'a.m.' or 'p.m.'

Teaching sequence

- Use these questions to check pupils' understanding of the 'a.m.' and 'p.m.' notation.

Unit 13 Time

 a It is 4 hours after midnight.

The time is 4:00 [a.m.]

b It is 2 hours after noon.

The time is 2:00 [p.m.]

c Mrs Philips goes to work in the morning.

She leaves home at 8:00 [a.m.]

Mrs Philips goes home after work in the evening.

She goes home at 5:00 [p.m.]

70

Activity

3 Look at the activities below.

Read and give the time shown on each clock with a.m. or p.m. Give reasons for all your answers.

Then arrange the times beginning with the earliest.

a

b

Hardeep wakes up

at (7:15 a.m.

Ella eats her lunch

at (12:20 p.m.

c

The fireworks display

ended at (8:10 p.m.

Teaching sequence

3

• This activity helps pupils to consolidate their understanding of reading and writing the time in 'a.m.' and 'p.m.'

Teaching sequence

- Ask pupils to make a list of their answers from **a** to **f** and arrange them in order, beginning with the earliest.

Activity

d

The children are at the fireworks display at 8:05 p.m.

e Peter has his breakfast at 7:50 a.m.

f

Mrs Kumar changes her son's nappy at 10:45 a.m.

Teaching sequence

4

- Assess pupils informally on their understanding of the use of 'a.m.' and 'p.m.'

5 *Maths Journal*

- Encourage pupils to write down the activities they carry out at specific times, and give the time in 'a.m.' or 'p.m.' for the listed activities.

---

4 Answer the questions with **a.m.** or **p.m.**

  a Ella plays football after school at 4:30 [p.m.]

  b Jack does his homework at 7:15 [p.m.] before he goes to bed.

  c Miya leaves home at 7:45 [a.m.] every day to go to school.

  d Peter goes out to play at 10:15 [a.m.]

Practice Book 2C, p.69

Maths Journal

5 Choose a day of the week. Now look at the times below. What do you do at these times? Write these in your book.

[8:00 a.m.] [10:00 a.m.] [noon] [1:00 p.m.]

When do you do the following?
Write in your book using a.m. or p.m.

[have a shower] [arrive at school] [watch TV] [sleep]

73

Learning objectives: Time taken in hours and minutes

Pupils will be able to:

- find the duration in terms of I hour or half an hour given start and end times
- find the start time given the end time and duration of I hour or half an hour
- find the end time given the start time and duration of I hour or half an hour

Key concepts

- 'Hour' is written as h and 'minutes' is written as mins.
- Time taken between two given times is measured in h and mins.

Thinking skill

Analysing time and event

What you will need

A clock face with minute and hour hands (see Photocopy master 9 on p 258)

Teaching sequence

- Show pupils 8 o'clock on the clock. Prompt them to read the time and ask a volunteer to write the time in numeral form and in words on the board.
- Next, show 9 o'clock by moving the hour hand to point at the number 9 on the clock. Ask pupils how much time is between 8 a.m. and 9 a.m.
- Move the minute hand one full circle around and point out to pupils that the answer is I hour.
- Write 'I h' on the board and get pupils to read in full: 'One hour'.
  Point out that I hr = I hour.

Unit I3 Time

Let's Learn!

Time taken in hours and minutes

1. Millie has a swimming lesson.
   Her swimming lesson starts at 8:00 a.m. and ends at 9:00 a.m.

Start
8:00 a.m.

End
9:00 a.m.

Lesson Time
I hour

9:00 a.m. is I h after 8:00 a.m.
8:00 a.m. is I h before 9:00 a.m.

What is **h**?

h stands for **hour**.

We read I h as one hour.

74

Ask pupils to work in pairs.

Pupil A gives a start time in hours
(a.m. or p.m) e.g. 5 a.m. They
then give a time in minutes, e.g.
25 minutes. Pupil B then says the
end time, e.g. 5.25 a.m.

Time **Unit 13**

2 Miya gets on the school bus at 3:00 p.m. and gets
home at 3:30 p.m.

How long is the ride home?

Start 3:00 p.m.	End 3:30 p.m.	Time taken 30 minutes

3:30 p.m. is 30 mins after 3:00 p.m.
3:00 p.m. is 30 mins before 3:30 p.m.

What is **mins**?

mins stands
for **minutes.**

We read 30 mins
as thirty minutes.

75

Teaching sequence

2

- Carry out the same activity as
  in **1** but this time show
  30-minute intervals, e.g., 6:00
  to 6:30. Prompt pupils to talk
  about duration and get them
  to read '30 mins' in full.

- Work through the examples
  in the textbook to familiarise
  pupils with duration.

Teaching sequence

3 and **4**

• Assess pupils informally on their ability to find the duration between two given times and give the start and end times.

---

3 Ruby arrives at the playground at 10:00 a.m. with her dad.

   Start   End

They leave the playground at 11:00 a.m.

They spend 1 h at the playground.

10:00 a.m. is 1 h before 11:00 a.m

11:00 a.m. is 1 h after 10:00 a.m.

4 Jack starts reading his book at 5:00 p.m.
He finishes reading his book 30 minutes or half an hour later.

He finishes reading at 5:30 p.m.

5:00 p.m. is half an hour before 5:30 p.m.

5:30 p.m. is half an hour after 5:00 p.m.

76

What you will need
- TV guide
- Photocopy master 10 (see p 259)

Time **Unit 13**

5 What is the time?

a 1 h after 8:00 p.m.
The time is 9:00 p.m.

b 1 h before 4:00 p.m.
The time is 3:00 p.m.

c 30 mins after 2:00 a.m.
The time is 2:30 a.m.

d 30 mins before 7:00 p.m.
The time is 6:30 p.m.

e 30 mins before noon.
The time is 11:30 a.m.

f 30 mins after noon.
The time is 12:30 p.m.

Activity

6 Use a TV guide to do this activity.
Look at the programmes shown from 2:00 p.m. to 8:00 p.m.

1 Find two programmes that are each 30 minutes long.

2 Find two programmes that are each 1 hour long.

3 Draw a chart like this and fill it in.

Programme	Start	End

Practice Book 2C, p.71

77

Teaching sequence

- Encourage pupils to practise telling the time, given an 1 h or 30 mins duration and using the terms 'before' and 'after'. E.g. 1 h after 10 a.m. is 11 a.m.

- Show pupils the TV guide and help them find programmes that last 1 hour or 30 minutes. Guide them to fill in the chart correctly.

Pupils will be able to:

- tell the correct time for a clock that is running slow
- tell the correct time for a clock that is running fast

Thinking skill

Analysing time and events

Independent work

Maths Journal, Challenging Practice, Problem Solving and *Review 5* in Practice Book 2C, pp 78 to 88.

Teaching sequence

7 *Put On Your Thinking Caps!*

- Point out to pupils that there can be more than one answer to both questions.

Unit 13 Time

7 **Put On Your Thinking Caps!**

Look at these clocks.

a

The clock is slow.
The actual time is after 8:00 p.m. on the same day.
Where do you think the hour hand could be?

It could be pointing anywhere from just after 8 to just before 12. It cannot be pointing at 12 because midnight is the next day.

b

The clock is fast.
The actual time is before 4:00 a.m. on the same day.
Where do you think the hour hand could be?

It could be pointing anywhere from 12 to just before 4.

There is more than one answer!

Practice Book 2C, p.79   Practice Book 2C, p.80

78

Unit 13 Time

Date: _____

Practice 1 The minute hand

1 Write the correct number of minutes in the boxes.

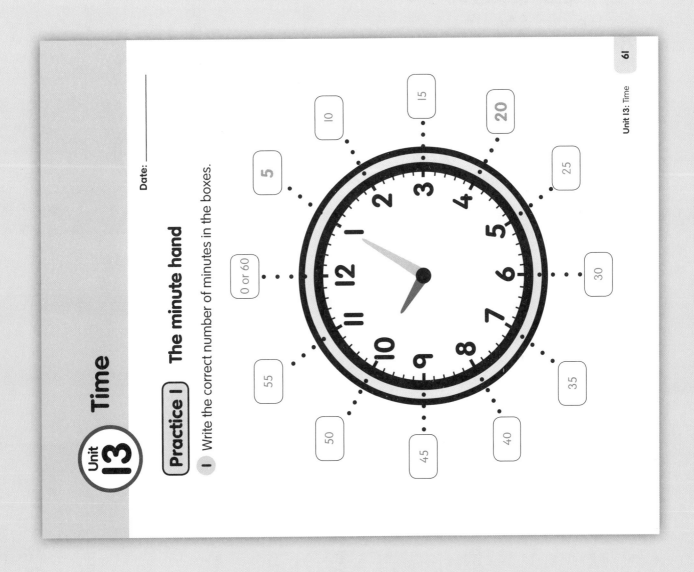

0 or 60
5
10
15
20
25
30
35
40
45
50
55

2 Fill in the spaces.

Example

The minute hand is showing __30__ minutes.

The minute hand is the long hand.

a The minute hand is showing __35__ minutes.

b The minute hand is showing __20__ minutes.

c The minute hand is showing __55__ minutes.

3 How many minutes does the minute hand show?

a __10 minutes__

b __40 minutes__

c __55 minutes__

d __25 minutes__

4 What is the time?

a __3 o'clock__   __5__ minutes past 3 o'clock.

b __7 o'clock__   __20__ minutes past 7 o'clock.

c __10 o'clock__   __45__ minutes past 10 o'clock.

What is the time now?

Practice 2   Reading and writing the time

1   What is the time?

Example

The time is _____7:40_____ .

a

The time is _____1:45_____ .

b

The time is _____2:00_____ .

c

The time is _____6:20_____ .

d

The time is _____9:05_____ .

e

The time is _____2:55_____ .

---

5   Draw the minute hand to show the time on the clock.

a   4:15

b   6:40

c   1:50

d   10:35

3 Draw the hour hand to show the time on the clock.

a

The time is 10:00.

b

The time is 11:30.

c

The time is 7:15.

d

The time is 4:20.

e

The time is 2:50.

f

The time is 3:40.

2 Draw the minute hand to show the time on the clock.

a

The time is 3:55.

b

The time is 6:30.

c

The time is 10:15.

d

The time is 8:00.

e

The time is 12:40.

f

The time is 9:05.

Date: _____

Practice 3 Learning a.m. and p.m.

I Write **a.m.** or **p.m.** in the spaces.

a

Omar wakes up at 7:30 _____ a.m.

b

He has his breakfast at 7:50 _____ a.m.

c

Omar goes cycling in the
afternoon at 3:30 _____ p.m.

---

4 Draw the hands on the clocks to show each time.

a

The time is 7:15.

b

The time is 4:30.

c

The time is 1:20.

d

The time is 9:25.

e

The time is 7:00.

f

The time is 9:50.

Practice 4 Time taken in hours and minutes

I Write **before** or **after** in the spaces.

Example

is I hour __before__

---

a

is I hour __after__

b

is I hour __before__

c

is I hour __after__

d  At 6:30 __p.m.__ Omar and his sister eat their dinner.

e 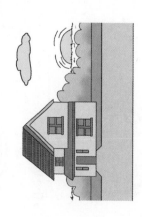 The sun sets at about 7:25 __p.m.__

f Omar's uncle likes to run at night.
He runs at 7:30 __p.m.__

3 Write the correct time in each box.
Check by drawing the hands on the clock.

Example

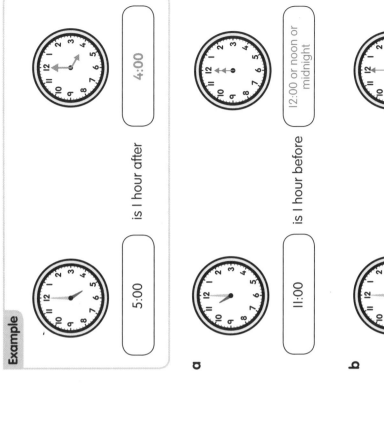

5:00   is 1 hour after   4:00

a   11:00   is 1 hour before   12:00 or noon or midnight

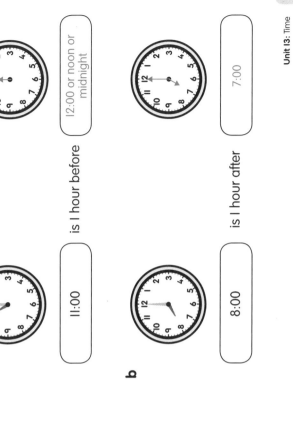

b   8:00   is 1 hour after   7:00

---

2 Write **before** or **after** in the spaces.

Example

is 30 minutes ___**before**___

a   is 30 minutes ___after___

b   is 30 minutes ___after___

c   is 30 minutes ___before___

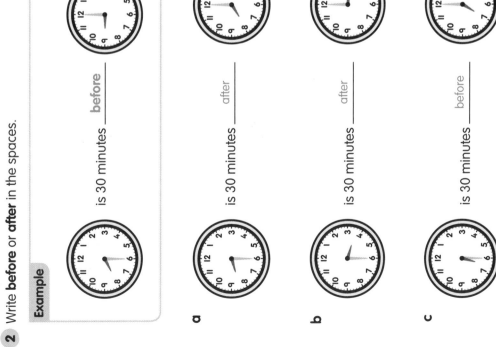

5 Draw the hands on the clock and write the time.

Example

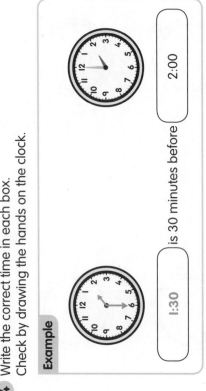

11:30 is 30 minutes after 11:00

a

8:30 is 30 minutes before 9:00

b

7:00 is 1 hour after 6:00

4 Write the correct time in each box.
Check by drawing the hands on the clock.

Example

1:30 is 30 minutes before 2:00

a

8:30 is 30 minutes after 8:00

b

9:30 is 30 minutes before 10:00

6 Write **before** or **after** in the spaces.
Then draw the hands on the clock.

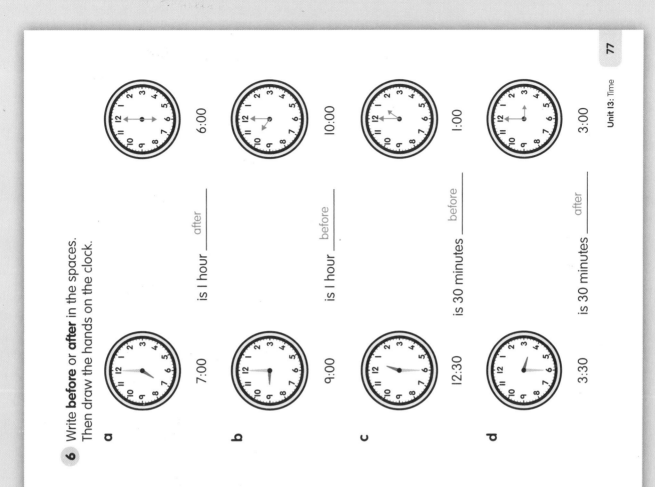

a

7:00

is 1 hour _after_

6:00

b

9:00

is 1 hour _before_

10:00

c

12:30

is 30 minutes _before_

1:00

d

3:30

is 30 minutes _after_

3:00

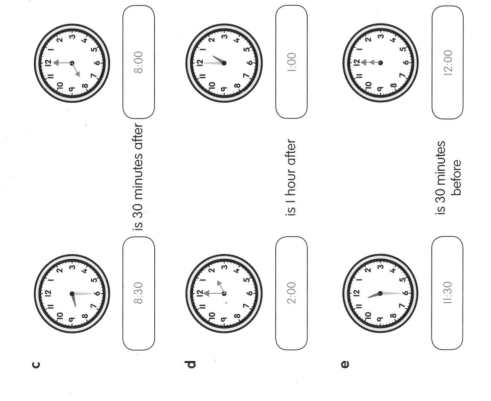

c

8:30

is 30 minutes after

8:00

d

2:00

is 1 hour after

1:00

e

11:30

is 30 minutes before

12:00

Maths Journal

Date: _____

1. Jack and Farha have made some mistakes. Can you help them?

a.   Jack wrote: The time is 4:25.
Write the correct time.

The time is 5:25.

b.   Farha moved the hands on the clock
to show 7:55.
This is what she did.
Is she correct? No
If she is not, redraw the hands on the
empty clock.

Challenging Practice

1. This clock is 1 hour slow.
What is the actual time?

The actual time is ___5:00___.

2. This clock is 30 minutes fast.
What is the actual time?

The actual time is ___5:30___.

3. This clock is 30 minutes slow.
What is the actual time?

The actual time is ___9:30___.

4. This clock is 1 hour fast.
What is the actual time?

The actual time is ___6:00___.

Date: _____

1 Which of the following shows $\frac{1}{3}$ correctly?

Tick (✓) the correct shapes.

 ✓

 ✓

2 Fill in the spaces.

a

The circle is divided into __8__ equal parts.

$\frac{3}{8}$ of the circle is shaded.

b

The shape is divided into __6__ equal parts.

$\frac{4}{6}$ of the shape is shaded.

Problem Solving

Date: _____

1 What time did Hardeep finish his homework?
Use the clues below to find out.

> Hardeep spent 1 hour writing his story.
> He took another 30 minutes to colour the pictures.
> Hardeep started his homework at 5:00 p.m.

1 hour after 5:00 p.m. is 6:00 p.m.
30 minutes after 6:00 p.m. is 6:30 p.m.
Hardeep finished his homework at 6:30 p.m.

 5:00 p.m.

1 h later

 6:00 p.m.

30 mins later

 6:30 p.m.

3 Ruby cuts a pizza into 8 equal pieces.
She eats 3 pieces.
What fraction of the pizza does she have left? $\frac{5}{8}$

4 Colour the shape to show the fractions. Answers vary

a
$\frac{5}{9}$

b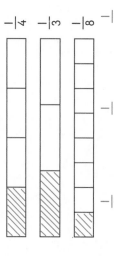
$\frac{2}{8}$

5 Colour $\frac{2}{7}$ of the shape red.

Colour $\frac{3}{7}$ of the shape blue.

What fraction of the shape is coloured? $\frac{5}{7}$

What fraction of the shape is not coloured? $\frac{2}{7}$

6 a Colour the strips.
Arrange the fractions in order, beginning with the greatest.

$\frac{9}{10}$

$\frac{7}{10}$

$\frac{2}{10}$

$\frac{9}{10}$, $\frac{7}{10}$, $\frac{2}{10}$
greatest

b Colour the strips.
Arrange the fractions in order, beginning with the greatest.

$\frac{1}{4}$

$\frac{1}{3}$

$\frac{1}{8}$

$\frac{1}{3}$, $\frac{1}{4}$, $\frac{1}{8}$
greatest

c Arrange the fractions in order, beginning with the smallest.

$\frac{1}{2}$, $\frac{1}{10}$, $\frac{1}{7}$, $\frac{1}{9}$

$\frac{1}{10}$, $\frac{1}{9}$, $\frac{1}{7}$, $\frac{1}{2}$
smallest

7 What fractions of the boxes are shaded? Fill in the spaces.

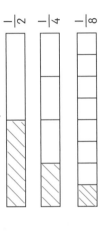

$\frac{2}{6}$

$\frac{3}{6}$

$\frac{4}{6}$

$\frac{5}{6}$

$\frac{6}{6}$ or 1

Use your answers above to help you answer these questions.

a $\frac{2}{6}$ is 2 out of 6 equal parts.

b $\frac{6}{6}$ or 1 is 6 out of 6 equal parts.

c _____ is greater than _____. Answers vary

d _____ is smaller than $\frac{2}{6}$. Answers vary

e $\frac{2}{6}$ is the smallest fraction.

f $\frac{6}{6}$ or 1 is the greatest fraction.

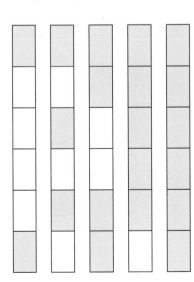

---

8 Colour the strips. Then fill in the spaces.

$\frac{1}{2}$

$\frac{1}{4}$

$\frac{1}{8}$

Which fraction is the smallest? $\frac{1}{8}$

Which fraction is the greatest? $\frac{1}{2}$

9 Add or subtract the fractions.

a $\frac{1}{7} + \frac{3}{7} = \frac{4}{7}$

b $\frac{3}{8} + \frac{2}{8} = \frac{5}{8}$

c $\frac{2}{9} + \frac{2}{9} + \frac{5}{9} = \frac{9}{9}$ or 1 whole

d $\frac{4}{5} - \frac{2}{5} = \frac{2}{5}$

e $\frac{7}{9} - \frac{5}{9} = \frac{2}{9}$

f $1 - \frac{7}{10} = \frac{3}{10}$

10 Tai ate $\frac{3}{7}$ of a loaf of bread.

Miya ate $\frac{1}{7}$ of the same loaf of bread.

How much more of the loaf of bread did Tai eat than Miya?

$\frac{3}{7} - \frac{1}{7} = \frac{2}{7}$

Tai ate $\frac{2}{7}$ more of the loaf of bread than Miya.

11 Fill in the spaces.

a

____30____ minutes
after 9 o'clock

b

____1____ hour
after 2 o'clock

12 What is the time shown on the clocks?

a

Time: ____6:15____

b

Time: ____12:50____

13 Draw the missing hands to show the correct times.

a

9:30

b

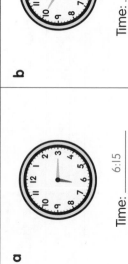

1:25

14 Fill in the spaces with **a.m.** or **p.m.**

a Farha brushes her teeth at 7:30 ___p.m.___ before she goes to sleep.

b Jack woke up in the night.
He went back to sleep at 2:45 ___a.m.___ .

15 Fill in the spaces with **before** or **after**.

a 8:30 a.m. is 30 minutes ___after___ 8:00 a.m.

b 2:30 p.m. is 30 minutes ___before___ 3:00 p.m.

c 9:00 a.m. is 1 hour ___before___ 10:00 a.m.

d 5 o'clock is 1 hour ___after___ 4 o'clock.

16 Fill in the spaces with **1 hour** or **30 minutes**.

a 3:00 a.m. is ___1 hour___ before 4:00 a.m.

b 6:30 p.m. is ___30 minutes___ after 6:00 p.m.

c 12 noon is ___1 hour___ after 11:00 a.m.

d 8:30 p.m. is ___30 minutes___ before 9:00 p.m.

17 Fill in the spaces with the correct times.

a 3:30 p.m. is 30 minutes before ___4:00 p.m.___ .

b 9:30 a.m. is 30 minutes after ___9:00 a.m.___ .

c 1:00 p.m. is 1 hour after ___12:00 p.m./noon___ .

d 11:00 a.m. is 1 hour before ___12:00 p.m./noon___ .

Week	Learning Objectives	Thinking Skills	Resources
1	**(1) Getting to know volume:** *Understanding volume* Pupils will be able to: • understand and explain that the volume of a liquid is the amount of that liquid in a container • understand that the volume of water is conserved no matter which container is used to contain the water *Comparing volumes* Pupils will be able to: • compare the volumes of liquids in identical containers by comparing the levels of liquid in the containers • compare levels of liquids in identical containers to determine which container has the most or least liquid • compare the volumes of water in identical containers and arrange them in ascending or descending order • compare the amounts of water in identical or non-identical containers by counting the number of non-standard units (glasses) that fill each container	• Spatial visualisation (conceptualising volume of liquid) • Comparing	• Pupil Textbook 2B, pp 79 to 84 • Practice Book 2D, pp 5 to 10 • Teacher's Guide 2B, pp 137 to 142

Unit 14: Volume

Week	Learning Objectives	Thinking Skills	Resources
1	**(2) Measuring in litres** Pupils will be able to: • state that the unit of measurement for volume is the litre (ℓ) • know how much 1 litre of liquid is and give examples of containers that can contain 1 litre of liquid • compare a measuring cylinder with 1 litre of liquid with another cylinder with more/less liquid • estimate the number of litres of water a container can hold and then check by measuring with 1 ℓ containers • use a scale on a container to find the volume of water it contains in litres	• Comparing and visualising volumes	• Pupil Textbook 2B, pp 85 to 88 • Practice Book 2D, pp 11 to 14 • Teacher's Guide 2B, pp 143 to 146

Medium-term plan

Week	Learning Objectives	Thinking Skills	Resources
1	**(3) Addition and subtraction of volumes** Pupils will be able to: • solve problems by relating the problems to addition and subtraction concepts such as 'part-whole', 'adding on', 'taking away' and 'comparing' • draw models to help solve one-step word problems • solve two-step word problems involving the use of addition and subtraction concepts • draw models to help solve two-step word problems	Applying concepts of addition and subtraction	• Pupil Textbook 2B, pp 89 to 91 • Practice Book 2D, pp 15 to 16 • Teacher's Guide 2B, pp 147 to 149
2	**(4) Multiplication and division of volumes** Pupils will be able to: • solve problems by relating them to multiplication and division concepts such as 'group and item' and 'multiplying' • draw 'part-whole' models to help solve one-step word problems	Applying concepts of multiplication and division	• Pupil Textbook 2B, pp 92 to 93 • Practice Book 2D, pp 17 to 18 • Teacher's Guide 2B, pp 150 to 151
2	*Put On Your Thinking Caps!* Pupils will be able to use 'drawing a diagram', comparing and deduction to solve problems.	• Comparing • Deduction Heuristic for problem solving: Draw a diagram	• Pupil Textbook 2B, p 94 • Practice Book 2D, pp 19 to 20 • Teacher's Guide 2B, p 152

Volume

Learning objectives:
Getting to know volume (understanding volume)

Pupils will be able to:

- understand and explain that the volume of a liquid is the amount of that liquid in a container
- understand that the volume of water is conserved no matter which container is used to contain the water

Key concepts

- The capacity of a container is the amount of space it can hold.
- The volume of a container is the amount of space it contains.

Thinking skills

- Spatial visualisation (conceptualising volume of liquid)
- Comparing

What you will need

- Containers of different sizes
- Water

Teaching sequence

- Ask pupils to fill empty containers of different sizes with coloured water as shown in the textbook.
- Introduce the terms 'volume' and 'capacity' and point out the differences.
- Point out to pupils that the amount of water in the container is called the volume of water. Encourage pupils to use this term.

Unit 14 Volume

Let's Learn!

Getting to know volume

Understanding volume

Let's fill these containers with coloured water.

Now each container has an amount of coloured water.

The amount of water is called the **volume** of water.

79

Liquid and 3 containers of different sizes for each group of pupils

Additional activity

Show pupils different containers filled with water.

Ask pupils what is inside the containers, and point out that they are all liquids.

Prompt pupils to note that liquids have volumes and the amount of liquid in a container is its volume.

Teaching sequence

- Ask pupils to work in groups. Give each group 3 containers of different sizes.
- Use this activity to make pupils aware of the conservation of volume.

Unit 14 Volume

Activity

2 You will need three empty containers of different sizes.

Example

1 Fill one container with some water.
Mark the level of water on the container.

2 Pour the water into another container.
Has the volume of water changed?
Pour the water back into the first container to check.

3 Now pour the water into a third container.
Has the volume of water changed?
How can you check?

The volume of water remains the same even when it is poured into different containers.

80

Pupils will be able to:

- compare the volumes of liquids in identical containers by comparing the levels of liquid in the containers
- compare levels of liquids in identical containers to determine which container has the most or least liquid
- compare the volumes of water in identical containers and arrange them in ascending or descending order
- compare the amounts of water in identical or non-identical containers by counting the number of non-standard units (glasses) that fill each container

What you will need

2 similar containers filled with liquid

Additional activity

Help pupils to fill 2 containers that hold different amounts of water.

Ask them to discuss methods they can use to find out if the containers have the same or different amounts of water in them.

Comparing volumes

 Bottles A and B are the same.

 Bottles A and B contain the same amount of water.

A   B

Bottle A contains **as much** water **as** Bottle B.

 Containers C and D are the same.

 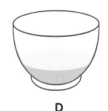

C   D

 What can you say about the volume of water in Containers C and D?

 The volume of water in Container C is more than the volume of water in Container D.

 The volume of water in Container D is less than the volume of water in Container C.

81

Teaching sequence

3

- Fill up 2 identical bottles with the same amount of water.
- Explain and show how the two bottles have the same volume of water, and discuss with pupils different ways to find out whether the amount of water is the same in the two bottles.

4

- Explain and show pupils that container C has a greater volume of water than container D.
- Discuss with pupils different ways to compare the amount of water, e.g., using a standard measuring cylinder.

Teaching sequence

- Use this question to check whether pupils can compare the volume in more than 2 identical containers.

5 Ella pours squash into four identical bottles.

A	**B**	**C**	**D**

Does Ella pour the same amount of squash into each bottle?

Which bottle has the most amount of squash? [C]

Which bottle has the least amount of squash? [B]

Bottle [B] has less squash than Bottle D.

The volume of squash in Bottle D is less than the volume of squash in Bottles [A] and [C].

The volume of squash in Bottle A is greater than the volume of squash in Bottles [B] and [D].

The volume of squash in Bottle A is less than the volume of squash in Bottle [C].

82

What you will need

5 identical glasses and coloured liquid

Additional activities

- Ask pupils to work in small groups. Give each pupil a similar container and ask them to fill it with some water.

  Ask pupils to arrange their containers in ascending or descending order according to the volumes of water in their containers.

- Fill several containers of different shapes with water. Ask pupils if they can tell which container contains the most water. Discuss how they can compare:

  (a) by pouring all the water from each container into one common container in turn and marking the level of each for comparison

  (b) by pouring all the water into smaller identical glasses, filling them to the brim, and counting the number of glasses for comparison

Volume **Unit 14**

Activity

6 You will need five identical glasses.
Pour different amounts of water into each glass.
Arrange the glasses in order.
Begin with the glass containing the smallest volume of water.

Show your answer by drawing on a piece of paper.

Did you know that you can make music with glasses of water?

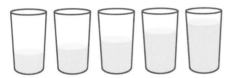

7 Peter fills glasses with all the water from Container A and Container B.

Container A

Container A contains less water than Container B.

Container B

Container B contains more water than Container A.

 Home Maths Ask your child to fill a glass with a small amount of water. Then get them to wet their finger and move their finger round the rim of the glass. Next add more water to the glass. Get them to move their finger round the rim. Repeat this a few times. Encourage them to make the connection between the volume of water and the pitch of the sound produced. The more water, the higher the sound.

83

Teaching sequence

6

- Pour different amounts of water into 5 identical glasses.
- Ask pupils to arrange the glasses in increasing order of volume.

7

- Point out to pupils that this activity provides another method of determining which container has more or less water.
- Explain that each full glass of water is a non-standard unit of measurement.

Independent work
Practice I and Practice 2 in
Practice Book 2D, pp 5 to I0.

Teaching sequence

- Use this question to check whether pupils can compare volumes.

Unit I4 Volume

⑧ Farha fills glasses with all the water from Jug A, Jug B and Jug C.

Jug A

Jug B

Jug C

Jug [B] contains the least amount of water.

Jug [C] contains more water than Jug A.

Jug C contains [7] more glasses of water than Jug B.

Jug B contains [3] fewer glasses of water than Jug A.

Practice Book 2D, pp. 5 and 7

84

Pupils will be able to:

- state that the unit of measurement for volume is the litre (ℓ)
- know how much I litre of liquid is and give examples of containers that can contain I litre of liquid
- compare a measuring cylinder with I litre of liquid with another cylinder with more/ less liquid
- estimate the number of litres of water a container can hold and then check by measuring with I ℓ containers
- use a scale on a container to find the volume of water it contains in litres

Key concept

The litre (ℓ) is a unit of measurement for volume.

Thinking skill

Comparing and visualising volumes

What you will need

- I ℓ container/beaker
- Containers of different sizes

Volume **Unit 14**

Let's Learn!

Measuring in litres

This is a carton of milk. It contains Iℓ of milk.

This is a glass of milk. It contains less than Iℓ of milk.

 ℓ stands for **litre**.

 We use litre (ℓ) to measure the volume of liquid.

 We read Iℓ as I litre.

2 These are some containers which hold less than I litre of liquid.

Can you think of other containers that hold less than I litre of liquid?

85

Teaching sequence

1

- Ask pupils to recall what the units of measurement for length and mass are (m and cm, kg and g respectively).
- Tell pupils that the unit of measurement for volume is the litre, and introduce the symbol 'ℓ'.
- Show pupils a I litre milk carton and pour out all its contents into a transparent container. Explain to pupils that the volume of the milk is I litre or I ℓ.
- Then show pupils a smaller container which contains less milk, and point out that the volume of milk in the smaller container is less than I litre.

2

- Show pupils some containers filled with less than I litre of liquid.
- Use any method to show that the volume of water is less than I litre, e.g., pouring out into a measuring cylinder or beaker.

Ask pupils to work in small groups. Show pupils different volumes of water in different containers, and ask them to guess whether the volumes are less than or more than I ℓ.

Ask them to fill up a measuring cylinder that has a volume of more than I ℓ. Then ask them to fill up a similar cylinder with a volume of less than I ℓ, and then compare the two.

What you will need

- Measuring cylinders
- Water
- Containers that hold more than I ℓ of liquid

Teaching sequence

- Show some containers filled with more than I litre of liquid.
- Use any method to show that the volume of liquid is more than I litre, e.g., pouring out into a measuring cylinder or beaker.

- Introduce a measuring cylinder that can measure more than I ℓ. Point out the markings on the cylinder.
- Fill up two identical measuring cylinders, one with more than I ℓ of water and the other with less than I ℓ. Encourage pupils to point out which one has more and which has less.
- Ask pupils to handle I ℓ containers to familiarise themselves with measuring I ℓ of liquids.

Unit 14 Volume

 These are some containers which hold more than I litre of liquid.

Can you think of other containers that can hold more than I litre of liquid?

This cylinder is used to measure the volume of liquid. It contains I litre of water.

Do the cylinders below contain **more than** or **less than** I litre of water?

This cylinder contains
more than I litre of water.

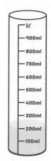

This cylinder contains
less than I litre of water.

86

What you will need

- A bucket with markings
- 1ℓ container
- Water
- Photocopy master 11
  (see p 260)

Volume **Unit 14**

5 This jug contains some squash.
Is the amount of squash more or less than I litre?
How can you check?

We can pour the squash into a 1ℓ measuring cylinder to check the volume of the squash.

Activity

6 Take a bucket. Add markings to it as shown.

Guess how many litres of water you will need to reach each mark.

Use a 1ℓ container to pour water into the bucket up to the different marks.
Count the litres of water as you pour.

Draw a chart like this and fill it in.

	My guess	Actual volume
A		
B		
C		

Are your guesses correct?

87

Teaching sequence

5

- Use this question to check pupils' ability to use measuring cylinders to determine whether the volume of squash is more than or less than 1ℓ.

6

- This activity helps pupils to consolidate their understanding of the concepts of volume, estimation and measuring of volume.

Teaching sequence

7

- Check whether pupils can read the litre markings on the container.

8

- Check whether pupils can read the litre scale on non-standard containers such as bottles and cups with litre markings.

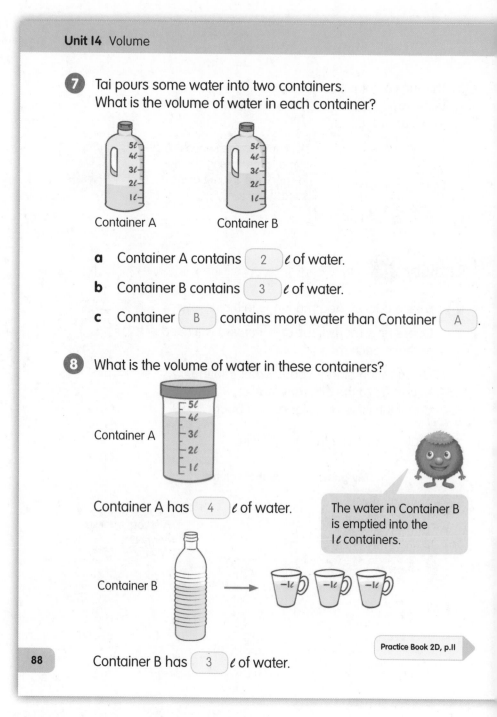

Unit 14 Volume

7 Tai pours some water into two containers.
What is the volume of water in each container?

Container A   Container B

a Container A contains [2] ℓ of water.

b Container B contains [3] ℓ of water.

c Container [B] contains more water than Container [A].

8 What is the volume of water in these containers?

Container A

Container A has [4] ℓ of water.

The water in Container B is emptied into the 1ℓ containers.

Container B

Container B has [3] ℓ of water.

Practice Book 2D, p.11

88

Pupils will be able to:

- solve problems by relating
  the problems to addition and
  subtraction concepts such
  as 'part-whole', 'adding on',
  'taking away' and 'comparing'
- draw models to help solve
  one-step word problems
- solve two-step word problems
  involving the use of addition
  and subtraction concepts
- draw models to help solve
  two-step word problems

Key concept

Volume in litres can be added
and subtracted like whole
numbers

Thinking skill

Applying concepts of addition
and subtraction

Volume **Unit 14**

Let's Learn!

Addition and subtraction of volumes

1 Hardeep has two bottles of orange juice.
He uses all the orange juice for his friends.

How much orange juice do his friends
drink altogether?

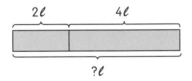

2 + 4 = 6

His friends drink 6ℓ of orange juice altogether.

2 The children are washing cars. They have 17ℓ of soapy water.
They use 8ℓ of the soapy water.

How much soapy water do the children have left?

 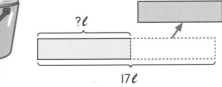  

17 − 8 = 9

The children have 9ℓ of soapy water left.

89

Teaching sequence

1 and **2**

- Ask pupils to read and
  understand the problem.
- Explain the underlying 'part-
  whole in addition' concept for
  1 and the 'taking away in
  subtraction' concept for **2**.
- Draw the models with all the
  necessary information filled in.
- Then, write the sentences to
  show pupils how to solve the
  problems.

Teaching sequence

- Use this question to check whether pupils can use concepts shown in ① and ② to solve one-step word problems.
- Note that the question is using the 'adding on' concept.

- Use this question to check whether pupils are able to apply the 'comparing in subtraction' concept to answer this question.

Unit 14 Volume

③ A water tank contains 34ℓ of water.
Omar fills up the tank with another 17ℓ of water.

How much water does the water tank contain now?

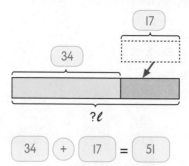

$$\boxed{34} \; \boxed{+} \; \boxed{17} \; = \; \boxed{51}$$

The tank contains $\boxed{51}$ ℓ of water now.

④ On Saturday, Family A uses 32ℓ of water.
Family B uses 28ℓ of water on the same day.

How much more water does Family A use than Family B?

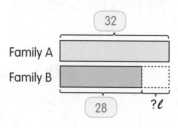

$$\boxed{32} \; \boxed{-} \; \boxed{28} \; = \; \boxed{4}$$

Family A uses $\boxed{4}$ ℓ more water than Family B.

90

Additional activity

Encourage pupils to draw models to reflect the different concepts in addition and subtraction; i.e. 'part-whole' concept, 'adding on' concept, 'taking away' concept and 'comparing' concept.

Then prompt them to write a story based on the model they have drawn.

Ask pupils to work in groups to write one-step word problems on addition or subtraction. Swap the problems between the groups and ask the groups to solve them.

Do the same with two-step word problems.

Ask pupils to draw models when solving the problems.

Practice 4 in Practice Book 2D, pp 15 to 16.

Volume **Unit 14**

5 Mr Brown has 98ℓ of milk to sell on Sunday.
He sells 15ℓ of milk in the morning and 42ℓ in the afternoon.

How many litres of milk does he have left?

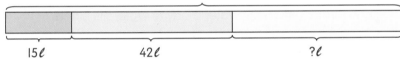

98ℓ

15ℓ   42ℓ   ?ℓ

15 + 42 = 57

First find the amount of milk Mr Brown sells.

Mr Brown sells 57 ℓ of milk.

98 − 57 = 41

Mr Brown has 41 ℓ of milk left.

6 Factory A uses 64ℓ of oil in a week.
Factory B uses 29ℓ of oil less than Factory A.

How many litres of oil do they use altogether?

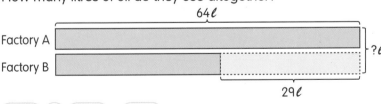

64ℓ

Factory A
                                        ?ℓ
Factory B

29ℓ

64 − 29 = 35

First find the amount of oil Factory B uses.

Factory B uses 35 ℓ of oil.

64 + 35 = 99

Factory A and Factory B use 99 ℓ of oil altogether.

Practice Book 2D, p.15   91

Teaching sequence

5

- Explain to pupils the underlying 'part-whole in addition' and 'taking away in subtraction' concepts for this question.
- Associate the term 'sells' with the 'taking away' concept.

6

- Use this question to check pupils' understanding. Explain the underlying 'adding on' and 'taking away' concepts if necessary.

Pupils will be able to:

- solve problems by relating them to multiplication and division concepts such as 'group and item' and 'multiplying'
- draw 'part-whole' models to help solve one-step word problems

Key concept

Volume in litres can be multiplied and divided like whole numbers.

Thinking skill

Applying concepts of multiplication and division

Teaching sequence

- Ask pupils to read and understand the word problem. Then explain the underlying 'group and item in multiplication' concept involved in the question.

- Use the question to check whether pupils are able to use the concept in ① to solve this problem.

Unit 14 Volume

Let's Learn!

Multiplication and division of volumes

① A farmer uses 5ℓ of water a day to water his plants.

How many litres of water does he use to water his plants in 7 days?

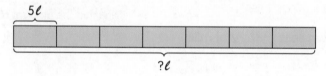

$7 \times 5 = 35$

He uses 35ℓ of water in 7 days.

② Millie collects 9 buckets of rainwater.
Each bucket contains 3ℓ of water.

How many litres of rainwater does Millie collect?

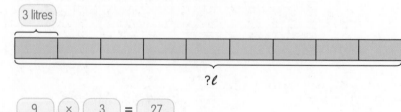

9 × 3 = 27

Millie collects 27 ℓ of rainwater.

92

Additional activity

Ask pupils to work in groups.

Ask them to write one-step word problems on multiplication and division and swap questions with other groups.

Encourage them to draw and label models to solve the questions.

Independent work

Practice 5 in Practice Book 2D, pp 17 to 18.

Volume **Unit 14**

3 A bowl contains 18ℓ of fruit punch.
Ruby pours all the fruit punch equally into 3 jugs.

How many litres of fruit punch does each jug contain?

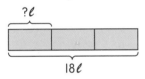

$18 \div 3 = 6$

Each jug contains 6ℓ of fruit punch.

4 Jack and his mum want to paint their garden fence.
They buy some tins of paint. Each tin contains 2ℓ of paint.
They use 14ℓ altogether.

How many tins of paint do they use?

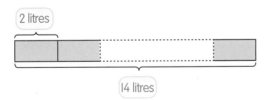

14 ÷ 2 = 7

Jack and his mum use   7   tins of paint altogether.

Practice Book 2D, p.17

93

Teaching sequence

- Help pupils to read and understand the problem. Explain the underlying 'group and item in division' concept, draw and label the model, then write a sentence to show pupils how to solve the problem.

- Use the question to check whether pupils can use the concept in **3** to solve one-step word problems.

Objective of activity

Pupils will be able to use 'drawing a diagram', comparing and deduction skills to solve problems.

Thinking skills

• Comparing
• Deduction

Heuristic for problem solving

Draw a diagram

Independent work

Challenging Practice and *Problem Solving* in Practice Book 2D, pp 19 to 20.

Teaching sequence

5 *Put On Your Thinking Caps!*

• Encourage pupils to draw models to help them solve the question.

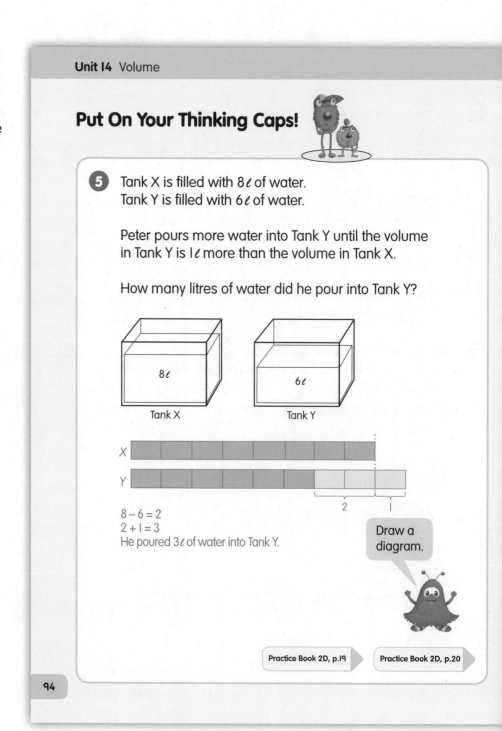

Unit 14 Volume

Put On Your Thinking Caps!

5 Tank X is filled with 8ℓ of water.
Tank Y is filled with 6ℓ of water.

Peter pours more water into Tank Y until the volume in Tank Y is 1ℓ more than the volume in Tank X.

How many litres of water did he pour into Tank Y?

8ℓ

Tank X

6ℓ

Tank Y

X

Y

2   1

8 − 6 = 2
2 + 1 = 3
He poured 3ℓ of water into Tank Y.

Draw a diagram.

Practice Book 2D, p.19   Practice Book 2D, p.20

94

Date: _____

Unit 14 Volume

Practice 1 Getting to know volume

1 Write **more** or **less** in the spaces.

a

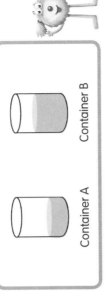

Container A   Container B

Container A and Container B are the same size.

Container B has __more__ water than Container A.

Container A has __less__ water than Container B.

b

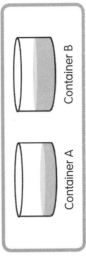

Container A   Container B

Container A and Container B are the same size.

Container A has __less__ water than Container B.

Container B has __more__ water than Container A.

Practice 2 **Getting to know volume**

Fill in the spaces.

1 Look at the cups of water that are poured into each container.

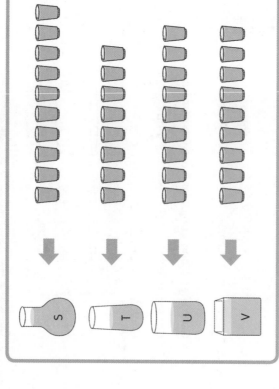

a Container __S__ has the most water.

b Container __T__ has the least water.

c Containers __U__ and __V__ have the same amount of water.

d Container __S__ has more water than Container U.

e Container V has less water than Container __S__.

2 Fill in the spaces.

a

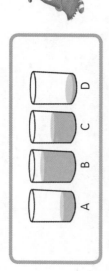

Container __B__ has the most water.

Container __D__ has the least water.

b

Container __D__ has the most water.

Container __C__ has the least water.

c

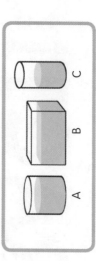

Container __B__ has the most water.

Container __C__ has the least water.

3 All the water in these containers is used to fill up the cups.

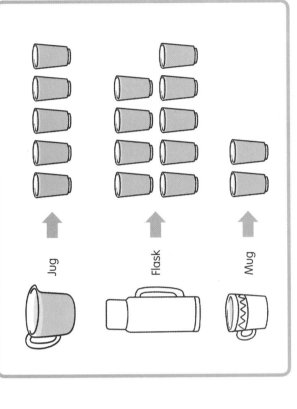

Jug

Flask

Mug

a The _____flask_____ has the most water.

b The _____mug_____ has the least water.

c There are ___4___ more cups of water in the flask than in the jug.

d There are ___7___ fewer cups of water in the mug than in the flask.

---

2 All the water in each container is used to fill up the beakers.

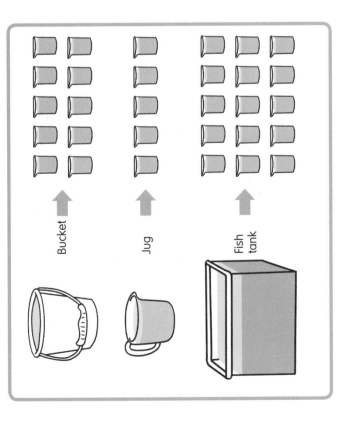

Bucket

Jug

Fish tank

a Which container has the greatest volume of water?
_____Fish tank_____

b Which container has the smallest volume of water?
_____Jug_____

c Which container has a greater volume of water, the bucket or the fish tank? _____Fish tank_____

d Which container has a smaller volume of water, the bucket or the jug? _____Jug_____

Date: _____

Practice 3 Measuring in litres

What is the volume of water in the containers?

Example

Volume of water = ___**1 litre**___ or ___**1 ℓ**___

1

Volume of water = ___2 litres___ or ___2 ℓ___

2

Volume of water = ___4 litres___ or ___4 ℓ___

4 Mr Hall has 4 kettles.
He uses all the water in the kettles to fill up the cups.

Kettle A

Kettle B

Kettle C

Kettle D

a Kettle ___A___ contains the most water.

b Kettle ___C___ contains the least water.

c Kettle A contains ___5___ more cups of water than
Kettle B.

d Kettle C contains 4 fewer cups of water than Kettle ___D___ .

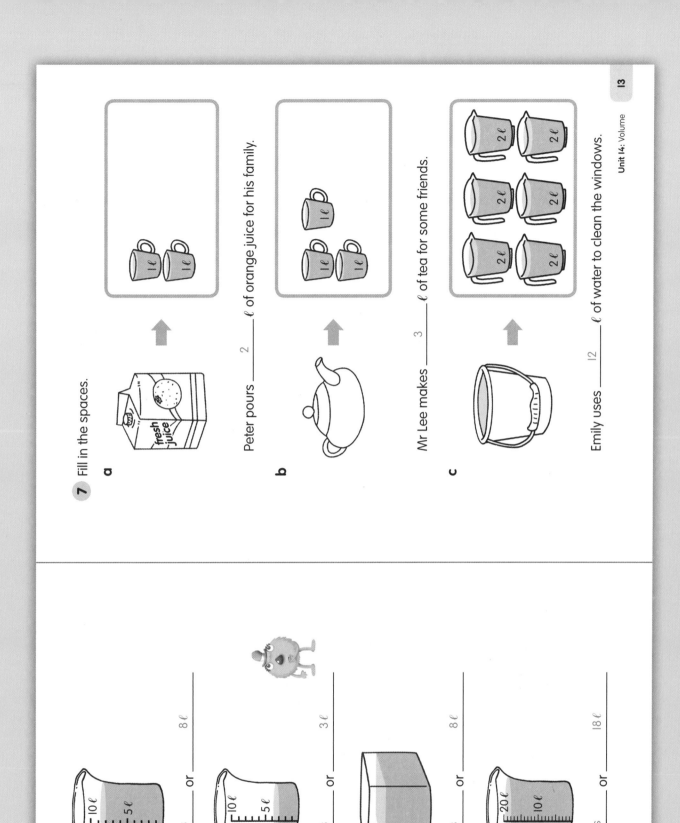

3

Volume of water = 8 litres or 8 ℓ

4

Volume of water = 3 litres or 3 ℓ

5

Volume of water = 8 litres or 8 ℓ

6

Volume of water = 18 litres or 18 ℓ

7 Fill in the spaces.

a

Peter pours 2 ℓ of orange juice for his family.

b

Mr Lee makes 3 ℓ of tea for some friends.

c

Emily uses 12 ℓ of water to clean the windows.

Practice 4 Addition and subtraction of volumes

Solve these word problems.

1 Miss Brook fills her car with 70 ℓ of petrol.
After driving to her friend's house, she only has 12 ℓ of petrol left.
How many litres of petrol does she use for the trip?

$70 - 12 = 58\,ℓ$

She uses ___58___ ℓ of petrol for the trip.

2 There are two tanks of water.
One tank contains 12 ℓ of water and another tank contains 7 ℓ of water.
What is the volume of water in the two tanks?

$12 + 7 = 19\,ℓ$

The volume of water in the two tanks is ___19___ ℓ.

8 Miya uses these volumes of juice to make fruit punch.
Write down the volume of each juice.

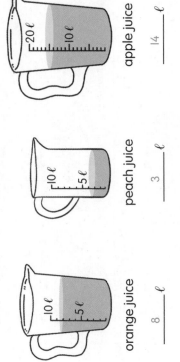

orange juice ___8___ ℓ

peach juice ___3___ ℓ

apple juice ___14___ ℓ

Arrange the volumes of the juice she used in order.
Begin with the smallest.

smallest ___3 ℓ___ , ___8 ℓ___ , ___14 ℓ___

Practice 5   Multiplication and division of volumes

Solve these word problems.

1 Ruby's family drinks 5 ℓ of juice in a week.
How many litres of juice does her family drink in 7 weeks?

7 × 5 = 35 ℓ

Her family drinks ___35___ ℓ of juice in 7 weeks.

2 Hardeep pours 18 ℓ of water equally into 3 buckets.
How much water is there in each bucket?

18 ÷ 3 = 6 ℓ

There are ___6___ ℓ of water in each bucket.

3 Mr Bell pours 32 ℓ of juice into some bottles.
Each bottle contains 4 ℓ of juice.
How many bottles does Mr Bell use altogether?

32 ÷ 4 = 8

Mr Bell uses ___8___ bottles altogether.

---

3 Ella fills two containers with water.
She fills Container A with 5 ℓ of water.
She fills Container B with 3 more litres of water than Container A.
How many litres of water does she use altogether?

3 + 5 = 8 ℓ
8 + 5 = 13 ℓ

She uses ___13___ ℓ of water altogether.

4 A tank holds 60 ℓ of rainwater.
On Saturday, 17 ℓ of rainwater is taken from it.
On Sunday, another 15 ℓ of rainwater is taken.
How much rainwater is left in the tank?

60 − 17 = 43 ℓ
43 − 15 = 28 ℓ

There is ___28___ ℓ of rainwater left in the tank.

5 Tai has three containers.
Container A holds 18 ℓ of water.
Container B holds 5 ℓ more water than Container A.
Container C holds 16 ℓ less water than Container B.
What is the volume of water in Container C?

5 + 18 = 23 ℓ
23 − 16 = 7 ℓ

There is ___7___ ℓ of water in Container C.

Challenging Practice

1 Look at the pictures.

bowl

2ℓ 2ℓ
2ℓ 2ℓ

bucket

How many bowls of water does it take to completely fill the bucket?

The bowl can hold 1 ℓ of water.
2 × 4 = 8 ℓ
The bucket can hold 8 ℓ of water.
It takes 8 bowls to completely fill the bucket.

---

4 Anna has 4 vases.
She fills each vase with 3 ℓ of water.
How much water is there in the vases altogether?

4 × 3 = 12 ℓ

There are ___12___ ℓ of water in the vases altogether.

5 Ruby drinks 2 ℓ of water each day.
How many days does she take to drink 14 ℓ of water?

14 ÷ 2 = 7

She takes ___7___ days to drink 14 ℓ of water.

6 Millie has 16 ℓ of water.
She pours equal volumes of water into 4 buckets.
How many litres of water are there in each bucket?

16 ÷ 4 = 4 ℓ

There are ___4___ ℓ of water in each bucket.

Problem Solving

1. Mrs Green runs a club after school.
Every day, she makes squash for the children at the club.
On the first day, she makes 2 ℓ of squash.
On the second day, she makes 1 ℓ more squash than on the first day.
Every day, she makes 1 ℓ more than the day before.

What is the volume of squash she makes on Day 5?

Make a list.

Day	Squash
1	2 ℓ
2	3 ℓ
3	4 ℓ
4	5 ℓ
5	6 ℓ

She makes 6 ℓ of squash on Day 5.

Week	Learning Objectives	Thinking Skills	Resources
2	**(1) Reading picture graphs** Pupils will be able to: • read and interpret picture graphs with scales in 1, 2, 3, 4, 5 or 10 • find the scale given the total number of items for a category and the number of units represented by each symbol • compare the differences between two or more types of items • find the sum of the number of items of two categories given in the picture graph • find the number of symbols to be drawn in the picture graph with sufficient information given	• Comparing • Classifying • Identifying relationships Heuristic for problem solving: • Guess and check	• Pupil Textbook 2B, pp 95 to 101 • Practice Book 2D, pp 21 to 24 • Teacher's Guide 2B, pp 165 to 171

Week	Learning Objectives	Thinking Skills	Resources
2 – 3	**(2) Making picture graphs** Pupils will be able to: • make picture graphs with scales in 1, 2, 3, 4, 5 or 10 • record items and make tables from information found in picture graphs • draw picture graphs with scales from the table, using appropriate scales for each picture graph • interpret information from picture graphs	• Comparing • Classifying • Identifying relationships • Sequencing	• Pupil Textbook 2B, pp 102 to 105 • Practice Book 2D, pp 25 to 30 • Teacher's Guide 2B, pp 172 to 175
3	**(3) More graphs** Pupils will be able to: • interpret graphs related to scale, make comparisons and find sums and differences • solve problems using picture graphs involving two variables	• Comparing • Classifying • Identifying relationships • Sequencing • Deduction • Inference	• Pupil Textbook 2B, pp 106 to 107 • Practice Book 2D, pp 31 to 34 • Teacher's Guide 2B, pp 176 to 177

Week	Learning Objectives	Thinking Skills	Resources
3	*Put On Your Thinking Caps!* Pupils will be able to: • read, understand and interpret the information in the picture graph given • use the given information to answer and explain higher order thinking skills questions	• Comparing • Classifying • Identifying relationships • Sequencing • Deduction • Inference	• Pupil Textbook 2B, pp 108 to 109 • Practice Book 2D, pp 35 to 36 • Teacher's Guide 2B, pp 178 to 179
	Review 6		• Practice Book 2D, pp 37 to 42

Summative assessment opportunity

Assessment Book 2, Test 7, pp 83 to 91

Graphs

Learning objectives: Reading picture graphs

Pupils will be able to:

- read and interpret picture graphs with scales in 1, 2, 3, 4, 5 or 10
- find the scale given the total number of items for a category and the number of units represented by each symbol
- compare the differences between two or more types of items

- find the sum of the number of items of two categories given in the picture graph
- find the number of symbols to be drawn in the picture graph with sufficient information given

Key concept

Picture graphs represented by symbols can be compared and interpreted.

Thinking skills

- Comparing
- Classifying
- Identifying relationships

What you will need

A selection of balls

Unit 15 Graphs

Let's Learn!

Reading picture graphs

1 Tai helps his teacher to put some balls in the storeroom.
There are four types of balls.
His teacher draws a picture graph to show the number of each type of ball.

Types of Balls in the Storeroom

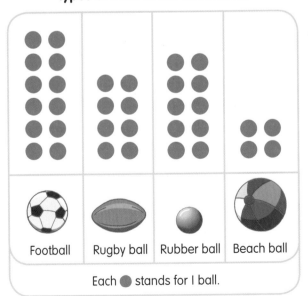

Each stands for 1 ball.

95

Teaching sequence

1

- Show pupils the different types of balls and relate them to the picture graph in the textbook.
- Briefly discuss the different types of balls and when they are used.
- Encourage pupils to look at the picture graph and ask volunteers to say what they understand from the graph.
- Pupils should be able to tell:
  - that each symbol stands for 1 ball
  - the number of each type of ball
  - the differences between the number of each type of ball
  - the total number of balls

Ask pupils to think of other objects that can be found in the classroom.

Ask them to draw a graph using a scale of I symbol to represent 3 units.

Then prompt pupils to find the number of objects in each category and in total.

Teaching sequence

- Explain and show that each symbol represents 2 balls, and that this information is indicated at the bottom of the picture graph.
- Pupils should be able to:
  - understand that each symbol stands for 2 balls
  - use skip-counting in twos to check the number of balls represented by each symbol and make comparisons
  - apply multiplication and division by 2

a
- Prompt pupils to multiply by 2 to find the number of footballs:
  I circle → 2 balls
  2 circles → 2 × 2 = 4 balls
  6 circles → 6 × 2 = 12 balls

b
- Encourage pupils to subtract to find how many more footballs than rugby balls there are. They can use different methods to find the answer.

Method I:
No. of footballs = 12
No. of rugby balls = 4 × 2 = 8
12 − 8 = 4

Method 2:
There are 2 more circles for footballs than rugby balls.
2 × 2 = 4
There are 4 more footballs than rugby balls.

Unit 15 Graphs

Tai redraws the graph.
Now he uses one ● to stand for 2 balls.

Types of Balls in the Storeroom

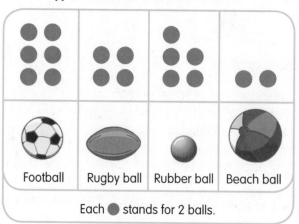

Each ● stands for 2 balls.

a How many footballs are there?

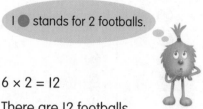

I ● stands for 2 footballs.

6 × 2 = 12

There are 12 footballs.

b How many more footballs than rugby balls are there?
There are 2 more ● for footballs than rugby balls.

2 × 2 = 4

There are 4 more footballs than rugby balls.

c How many footballs and rugby balls are there altogether?

12 + 8 = 20

or

10 × 2 = 20

There are 20 footballs and rugby balls altogether.

d

There are 10 of this type of ball.

Which type of ball is Tai talking about?

10 ÷ 2 = 5

There are 5 ● for this type of ball.

Tai is talking about rubber balls.

e Tai's teacher buys more beach balls.
The number of rubber balls and the number of beach balls are the same.
How many more beach balls does Tai's teacher buy?

There are 3 more ● for rubber balls than beach balls.

3 × 2 = 6

Tai's teacher buys 6 more beach balls.

97

Teaching sequence

c

- Discuss using addition to find the total number of footballs and rugby balls. Remind pupils to use the two methods in the textbook to find the answer.

d

- Remind pupils to use division to find the answer. Pupils can also use the 'guess and check' method to find the answer.

  Guess: The answer is beach ball.
  There are 2 circles for beach ball.
  2 × 2 = 4 but it is not equal to 10.
  So it is not correct.
  Guess: The answer is 'rubber ball'.
  5 × 2 = 10
  So the answer is rubber ball.

e

- Similar to **b**, encourage pupils to use the two methods to find the answer. Ask pupils to recall the methods before sharing the answer with them.

Ask pupils to carry out the same
activity from page 166.

Suggest that they draw the
graph horizontally instead of
vertically.

Teaching sequence

- Assess pupils informally to
  gauge whether they can use a
  graph with scales to answer
  the problem.
- Briefly talk about teeth. Ask
  pupils how many teeth they
  have lost.
- Ask pupils to look at and read
  the picture graph and discuss
  what information they can get
  from it.
- Pupils should be able to:
  - tell how many children lost
    one tooth each:
    1 item × 3 = 3 children
  - tell how many children lost
    three teeth each:
    2 items × 3 = 6 children
  - compare two sets of
    pictures which are the
    same
  - calculate the total number
    of children

Unit 15 Graphs

2 Peter's friends have lost some of their baby teeth.
He draws a picture graph to show the number of
children who have lost some of their teeth.

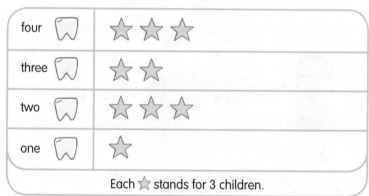

Number of Teeth Lost

- a 3 children have each lost only one tooth.
- b 6 children have each lost three teeth.
- c The number of children who have lost [two] teeth is
  the same as those who have lost [four] teeth.
- d Peter has [27] friends altogether.

 Explain to your child what baby teeth are. Talk about how many they have lost and how many
they still have to loose. Count the number of teeth they have and compare the number of teeth
children and adults have.

98

---

3 Miya's mum owns a pet shop.

She draws a picture graph to show the number of each type of pet in her shop.

Types of Pets in the Shop

🐢	Terrapin	▲ ▲ ▲
🐟	Fish	▲ ▲ ▲ ▲ ▲
🐹	Hamster	▲
🐰	Rabbit	
🐱	Cat	▲ ▲ ▲
🐦	Bird	▲ ▲ ▲ ▲ ▲ ▲

Use the graph to answer these questions.

a Miya's mum has 20 fish.

Each stands for (4) animals.

b She has (20) more birds than hamsters.

c There are (36) cats and birds altogether.

d She has I6 rabbits.

How many ▲ should there be on the graph? (4)

e She buys 8 more terrapins.

She has to draw (2) more ▲ on the graph.

99

Teaching sequence

3

- Talk through the graphs and questions with pupils. Ask them to answer the question first before discussing the correct answer.
- For **a**, pupils should be able to use division to determine the number represented by each symbol.
- There are five symbols representing fish. So 20 divided by 5 gives 4.

Teaching sequence

- Use the question to check whether pupils can use the strategies to interpret picture graphs and solve problems from ❶, ❷ and ❸.

❹ The children are at the wildlife park.
They draw a picture graph to show the number of each type of animal they see.

Animals at the Wildlife Park

a The children see 25 lions.

Each 🙎 stands for (5) animals.

b They see (10) more elephants than giraffes.

c They see 15 gorillas.
They have to draw (3) 🙎 on the graph.

d They see 10 tigers.
They have to draw (1) more 🙎 on the graph.

e There are (15) fewer giraffes than lions.

100

Practice I in Practice Book 2D,
pp 2I to 24.

Graphs **Unit I5**

5 Hardeep's dad sells fruit at his market stall.
He draws a picture graph to show the number of each type of
fruit he sold on Monday.

Fruit Sold on Monday

a   He sold 40 pears.

   Each stands for ⌈ 10 ⌉ pieces of fruit.

b   He sold 80 oranges.

   He has to draw ⌈ 8 ⌉ on the graph.

c   He sold ⌈ 40 ⌉ more apples than bananas.

d   The fruit that he sold the most was ⌈oranges⌉.

e   He sold ⌈ 250 ⌉ pieces of fruit altogether.

Practice Book 2D, p.2I

I0I

Teaching sequence

5

• Use the question to check
  whether pupils can use the
  strategies to interpret picture
  graphs and solve problems
  from **1**, **2** and **3**.

Learning objectives: Making picture graphs

Pupils will be able to:

- make picture graphs with scales in 1, 2, 3, 4, 5 or 10
- record items and make tables from information found in picture graphs
- draw picture graphs with scales from the table, using appropriate scales for each picture graph
- interpret information from picture graphs

Key concept

Picture graphs can be made using different symbols and scales.

What you will need

Counters

Thinking skills

- Comparing
- Classifying
- Identifying relationships
- Sequencing

Teaching sequence

- The objective of this section is to guide pupils to collect data and use it to draw a picture graph.
- Ask pupils to look carefully at the picture of Peter's uncle's farm in the textbook.
- Talk about the types and number of each animal in the picture.
- Compare the number of animals. You may want to display a picture graph of Peter's uncle's farm (without the symbols) on the board.
- Summarise the data and record it in the table as shown in the textbook.

Unit 15 Graphs

Let's Learn!

Making picture graphs

 Peter's uncle has a farm.
Peter counts each type of animal on the farm.

He then records the types of animals and the number of each animal in a chart.

Type of animal	Chicken	Cow	Duck	Sheep	Horse
Number	10	2	12	6	4

102

Additional activity

- The class could sing "*Old MacDonald Had A Farm*" as an introduction to this section.
- Play a recording of animal sounds to the class and ask them to guess each animal sound.

Peter draws a picture graph to show the number of each type of farm animal.

Types of Farm Animals

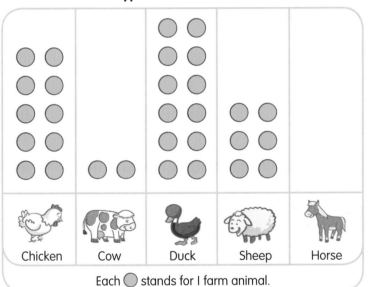

Each ◯ stands for 1 farm animal.

Use the graph to answer these questions.

a Peter's uncle has [5] types of farm animals.

b He has [10] chickens.

c He has [12] ducks.

d He has [6] sheep and [2] cows.

e Peter has to draw [4] ◯ to show the number of horses.

f Peter's uncle has [34] farm animals altogether.

Teaching sequence

- Explain to pupils that the picture graph is based on the recorded data and each symbol represents one animal.
- Interpret the picture graph and work through the questions with the class.

103

Unit 15: Graphs 173

A Surprise Bag containing pairs of red, yellow, blue, green, purple and orange coloured pencils (the pencils are bundled in pairs by colour)

Teaching sequence

- Note that each symbol stands for the same number of pencils in each bundle.
- Explain to pupils that each symbol in the picture graph represents two pencils because each bundle has two pencils.
- You could ask pupils how many pencils each circle represents if there are three pencils in each bundle.
- Carry out the steps for this activity and then ask pupils to complete the picture graph.

Unit 15 Graphs

Activity

2 Ella has a Surprise Bag with 12 coloured pencils.

The coloured pencils are bundled in pairs by colour.

Red   Yellow   Blue   Green   Purple   Orange

Ella takes out a pair of coloured pencils from her bag. It is an orange pair!

Each O stands for 2 coloured pencils.

She draws a ◯ on the graph to stand for the pair of orange coloured pencils.

She puts the pair of orange coloured pencils back into the bag.

104

Practice 2 in Practice Book 2D,
pp 25 to 30.

Graphs **Unit 15**

Activity

You have a Surprise Bag like Ella's.
Take out a pair of coloured pencils from the bag.
Copy the graph on a piece of paper.

Then draw a ◯ on the graph to stand for this pair of coloured
pencils.

Red		
Yellow		
Blue		
Green		
Purple		
Orange	◯	

Each ◯ stands for 2 coloured pencils.

Put the coloured pencils
back into the bag.
Do this ten more times.
Give your graph a title.
Show and explain your
graph to the class.

The graph shows the number
of each type of coloured pencil

Practice Book 2D, p.25

105

Teaching sequence

- Once the picture graph
  is finished, ask pupils to
  complete the sentence in the
  thought bubble.
- Invite volunteers to show
  their graphs to the class and
  explain them.

Pupils will be able to:

- interpret graphs related to scale, make comparisons and find sums and differences
- solve problems using picture graphs involving two variables

- Comparing
- Classifying
- Identifying relationships
- Sequencing
- Deduction
- Inference

Key concept

Interpreting picture graphs to solve problems

Teaching sequence

- Encourage pupils to read and interpret the picture graph and answer the questions.
- When explaining **c** and **d**, point out that the number of pupils here is made up of both boys and girls.
- Relate this question to the 'part-whole' concept in addition and subtraction.

Unit 15 Graphs

Let's Learn!

More graphs

1 The graph shows the number of children playing different types of games in school.

Types of Games Children Play

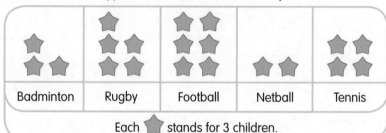

| Badminton | Rugby | Football | Netball | Tennis |

Each stands for 3 children.

Use the graph to answer these questions.

a How many children are playing rugby?

There are 〔 5 〕 for rugby.

〔 5 〕 × 〔 3 〕 = 〔 15 〕

〔 15 〕 children are playing rugby.

b How many children are playing football and netball altogether? 〔 24 〕

c 6 of the children playing badminton are girls.

There are 3 ⭐ for badminton.

How many boys are playing badminton?

〔 9 〕 – 〔 6 〕 = 〔 3 〕

〔 3 〕 boys are playing badminton.

Practice 3 in Practice Book 2D,
pp 3I to 34.

d I5 of the children playing football are boys.

How many girls are playing football? [3]

2 The graph shows the favourite fruit of children in a school.

Favourite Fruit

Apple	◆ ◆ ◆ ◆
Banana	◆ ◆
Kiwi	◆
Grapes	◆ ◆ ◆ ◆ ◆ ◆
Orange	◆ ◆ ◆ ◆ ◆

Each stands for 4 children.

Use the graph to answer these questions.

a 4 of the children who chose apples as their favourite
fruit are boys.
How many girls chose apples as their favourite fruit? [I2]

b I6 girls chose grapes as their favourite fruit.
How many boys chose grapes as their favourite fruit? [8]

c 4 girls chose bananas and 8 girls chose oranges as
their favourite fruits.
Altogether how many boys chose bananas and
oranges as their favourite fruit? [I6]

Practice Book 2D, p.3I

I07

Teaching sequence

2

- Use this question to check pupils' understanding.
- Ask pupils to look at the picture graph and discuss the information they can get from it.
- Point out that similar to **①**, the pupils in this question are made up of both girls and boys.

Objectives of activity

Pupils will be able to:

- read, understand and interpret the information in the picture graph given
- use the given information to answer and explain higher order thinking skills questions

Thinking skills

- Comparing
- Classifying
- Identifying relationships
- Sequencing
- Deduction
- Inference

Teaching sequence

3 *Put On Your Thinking Caps!*

- Begin by asking pupils to look at the picture graph.
- Ask them to write down the number of children on each type of ride, then to compare the number of children on each type of ride.

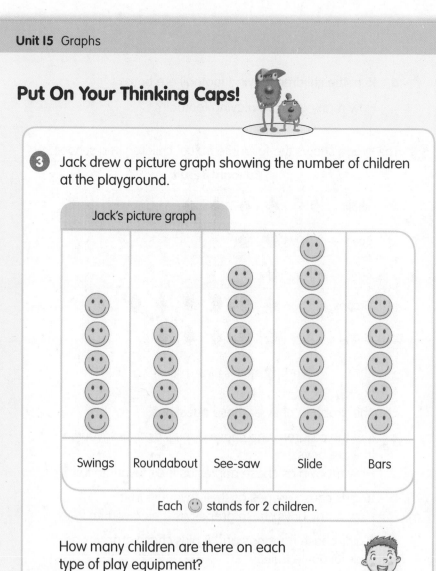

Unit 15   Graphs

Put On Your Thinking Caps!

3 Jack drew a picture graph showing the number of children at the playground.

Jack's picture graph

| Swings | Roundabout | See-saw | Slide | Bars |

Each 🙂 stands for 2 children.

How many children are there on each type of play equipment?

108

Independent work

Challenging Practice, Problem Solving and Review 6 in Practice Book 2D, pp 35 to 42.

Graphs **Unit 15**

Put On Your Thinking Caps!

Use the graph to answer these questions.

a How many children should move from the slide to the swings so that there are an equal number of children on both? 2

b How many more children should go on the roundabout so that there are 2 more children on the roundabout than on the bars? 4

c How many children should get off the slide so that there are an equal number of children on both the slide and the roundabout? 6

d How many children should get off the swings so that there are 4 more children on the see-saw than on the swings? 2

Practice Book 2D, p.35   Practice Book 2D, p.36

109

Teaching sequence

- Encourage pupils to use counters, or similar manipulatives, to show movements of children to help solve the problem.
- E.g. To find the answer for **a**, you need to show 7 counters representing children on the slide and 5 counters representing children on the swings. When you move 1 counter from the slide to the swings, there will be 6 counters in each group.

Unit 15 Graphs

Date: _____

Practice 1   Reading picture graphs

1 Jack and his friends pack some food for a picnic.
   The picture graph below shows the amount of food they packed.

Amount of Food Packed

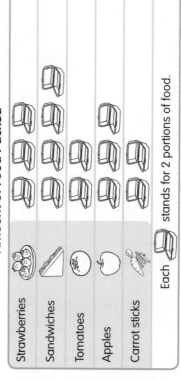

Strawberries	
Sandwiches	
Tomatoes	
Apples	
Carrot sticks	

Each 🥪 stands for 2 portions of food.

a They take ___6___ portions of strawberries.

b They take the same number of portions of ___apples___ as
   strawberries.

c They take ___4___ more portions of sandwiches than
   portions of carrot sticks.

d They take ___12___ portions of sandwiches and carrot
   sticks altogether.

a How many different fairy tale characters are shown?

_4_

b Who is the most popular fairy tale character?

Cinderella

c Who is the least popular fairy tale character?

Pinocchio

d 8 children like Rapunzel. What does each stand for?

2 children

e How many children chose Cinderella as their favourite character?

_14_ children

f How many more children chose Snow White than Rapunzel as their favourite character?

_4_ more children

g The total number of children who chose _Rapunzel_ and _Pinocchio_ as their favourite characters is the same as the number of children who chose Cinderella.

2 Farha and her classmates tell one another who their favourite fairy tale characters are.
This picture graph shows their choices.

Children's Favourite Fairy Tale Characters

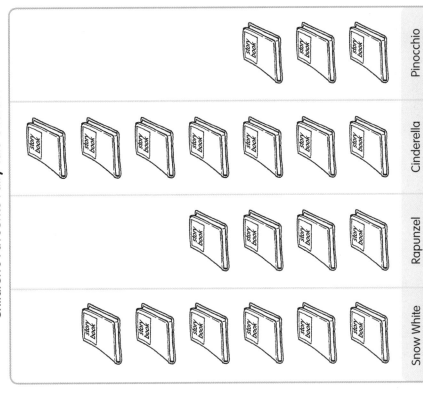

Practice 2   Making picture graphs

1 Peter buys some fruit juice from a supermarket.
   How many cartons of fruit juice of each type are on the shelves?

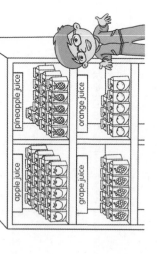

Count the cartons of fruit juice on the shelves.
Complete the graph.

Number of Cartons of Fruit Juice

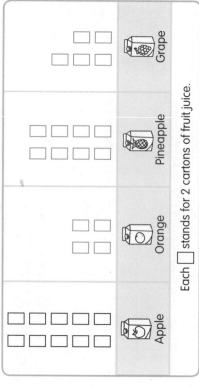

| Apple | Orange | Pineapple | Grape |

Each ⬜ stands for 2 cartons of fruit juice.

How many cartons of fruit juice are there altogether? ____54____

---

3 Omar's house is near a school, a bus stop, a shop
   and a post office.
   He draws a picture graph to show how far his house
   is from these places.

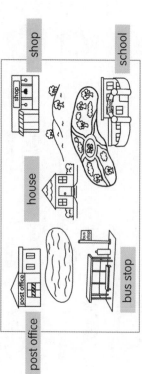

Number of Steps from Omar's House

| School |
| Shop |
| Bus stop |
| Post office |

a The school is 100 steps from Omar's house.
   Each 🚗 stands for __10__ steps.

b The shop is __90__ steps from Omar's house.

c Omar's house is 50 steps from the bus stop.
   He has to draw __5__ 🚗 on the graph.

d The post office is 80 steps from Omar's house.
   He has to draw __2__ more 🚗 on the graph.

d In the graph below, show the number of animals Mr Ali has by colouring the ◯.

Animals that Mr Ali Looks After

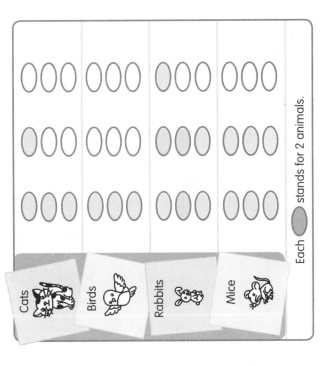

Each ⬭ stands for 2 animals.

---

2 Mr Ali looks after lots of animals.
The picture shows the animals he looks after.

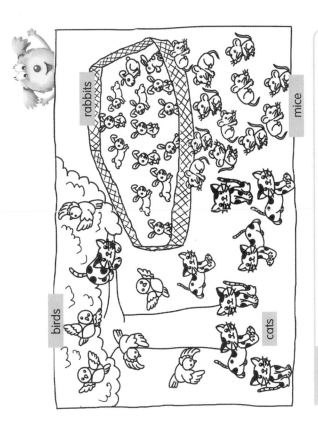

Example
How many cats are there? ___8___ cats

a How many birds are there? ___6___ birds

b How many rabbits are there? ___14___ rabbits

c How many mice are there? ___12___ mice

3 Ella and Hardeep make biscuits for a school fair.

Here are the biscuits they bake!

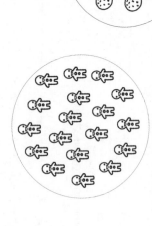

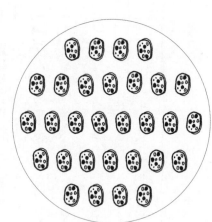

raisin biscuits

gingerbread men

chocolate chip biscuits

oat biscuits

iced biscuits

a Fill in the spaces.

They bake ___18___ gingerbread men,

___9___ raisin biscuits, ___15___ oat biscuits,

___12___ iced biscuits and ___30___ chocolate chip biscuits.

b Complete the picture graph below. Give it a title.

Title: _Biscuits Baked for a School Fair_

Raisin biscuits 🥚	
Oat biscuits	
Chocolate chip biscuits	⬤⬤ ⬤⬤ ⬤⬤ ⬤⬤ ⬤⬤
Gingerbread men	
Iced biscuits	

Each ◯ stands for 3 biscuits.

Date: _____

Practice 3 More graphs

1. Farha and her friends compare their sticker collections.
She draws a picture graph to show the number of stickers they have.
Then she spills her drink on part of the graph.

Number of Stickers

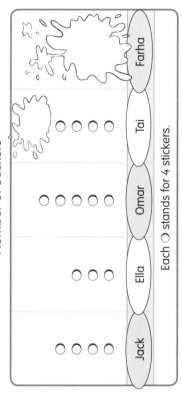

Jack	Ella	Omar	Tai	Farha

Each ○ stands for 4 stickers.

a How many stickers does Jack have? ___16 stickers___

b How many more stickers does Omar have than Ella?
___8 more stickers___

c Farha has 8 stickers.
How many ○ should there be on the graph? ___2___

d Tai has 24 stickers.
How many more ○ should there be on the graph? ___2___

e How many stickers do Jack and Ella have altogether?
___28 stickers___

Unit 15: Graphs   31

---

4 Ruby reads a book about outer space.
She dreams about all these things.

a Each 🚀 stands for 5 spaceships.

She dreams about ___25___ spaceships.

b Each 👨‍🚀 stands for 4 astronauts.

She dreams about ___16___ astronauts.

c Each 🪐 stands for 3 planets.

She dreams about ___9___ planets.

d Each 😊 stands for 10 flying rocks.

She dreams about ___40___ flying rocks.

Unit 15: Graphs

30

Answers Unit 15: Graphs   185

2 The graph shows the number of children playing at each game stall at a fun fair.

Number of Children at Each Game Stall

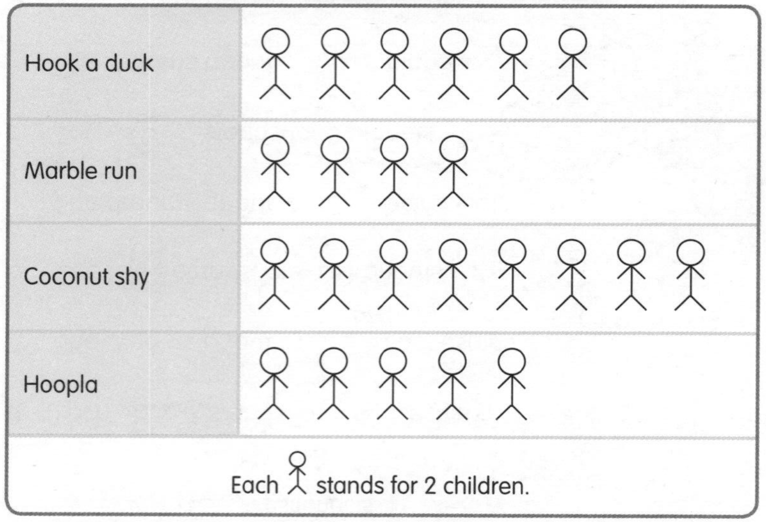

Hook a duck						
Marble run						
Coconut shy						
Hoopla						

Each ☿ stands for 2 children.

Use the graph to answer these questions.

a There are 6 boys at the hoopla stall.
How many girls are at the hoopla stall? ___4___

b 6 of the children who play at the coconut shy stall are girls.
How many of them are boys? ___10___

c 2 girls are at the marble run stall.
4 boys are at the hook a duck stall.
How many girls are at the marble run and hook a duck stalls altogether? ___10___

---

3 The graph shows the number of people at the cinema.

Number of People at the Cinema

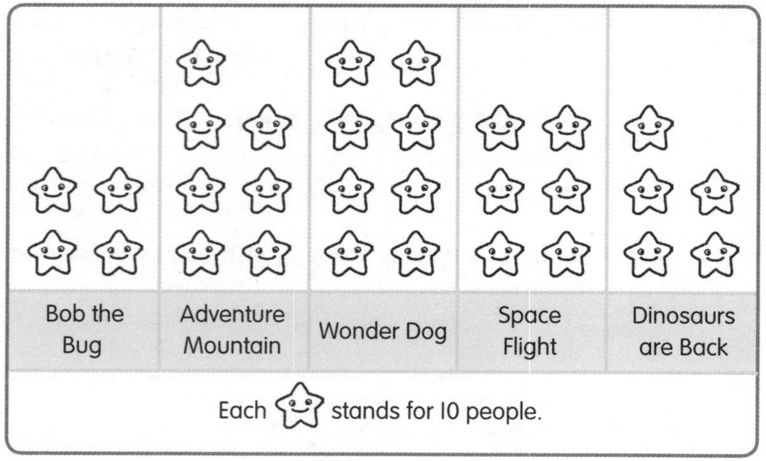

Bob the Bug	Adventure Mountain	Wonder Dog	Space Flight	Dinosaurs are Back

Each ⭐ stands for 10 people.

Use the graph to answer these questions.

a There are 60 adults watching Adventure Mountain.
How many children are watching Adventure Mountain?
___10 children___

b 60 adults are watching Space Flight.
How many children are watching Space Flight? ___0___

c 20 children are watching Wonder Dog and
40 children are watching Dinosaurs are Back.
How many adults are watching Wonder Dog and
Dinosaurs are Back? ___70 adults___

Date: _____

Challenging Practice

1 Mrs Green records the number of eggs she collects from her chickens every day for 3 days.

She draws a ◯ for every 2 eggs she collects.

1st day	2nd day	3rd day	4th day
◯	◯ ◯	◯ ◯ ◯ ◯	◯ ◯ ◯ ◯ ◯ ◯ ◯ ◯

The number of eggs Mrs Green collects follows a pattern.
If this pattern carries on, how many eggs will Mrs Green collect on the 4th day?

1st → 2 eggs
2nd → 4 eggs
3rd → 8 eggs
4th → 16 eggs

Mrs Green will collect ____16____ eggs on the 4th day.

---

4 Peter bakes a banana cake for his family.
Use the information given to complete the graph.

a Peter uses 2 cups of sugar.
He uses the same number of cups of butter.

b He uses 2 more cups of flour than the number of cups of milk.

c He uses 6 cups of mashed bananas.

Complete the graph using △ to stand for 2 cups.

Banana Cake Ingredients

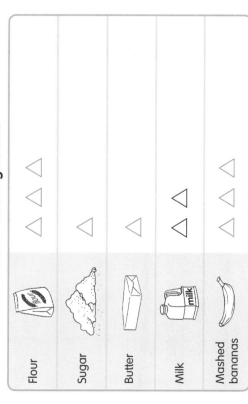

Flour	△ △ △
Sugar	△
Butter	△
Milk	△ △
Mashed bananas	△ △ △

Review 6

I Look at the pictures below.

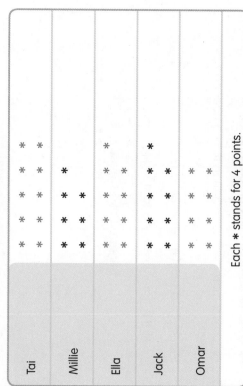

Container A   Container B

Which container has a greater volume of water? _____ Container B

2 Fill in the spaces.

A   B   C   D

a Which glass has the most water? _____ B

b Complete this sentence.

Glass __C__ contains as much water as Glass __D__ .

Problem Solving

I 5 children took part in a quiz.
The graph shows how many points they each scored.
Complete the graph using the information below.

Tai scored 40 points.
Omar scored 8 points fewer than Tai.
Ella and Jack scored the same number of points.

Points in the Quiz

Tai	*	*	*	*	*	*	*	*	*	*
Millie	*	*	*	*						
Ella	*	*	*	*	*	*				
Jack	*	*	*	*	*	*	*	*		
Omar	*	*	*	*						

Each * stands for 4 points.

3 Find the volume of water in each container.

Container A

Volume of water = _____ 5 litres _____ or _____ 5 ℓ _____

Container B

Volume of water = _____ 70 litres _____ or _____ 70 ℓ _____

Container C

Volume of water = _____ 40 litres _____ or _____ 40 ℓ _____

Container D

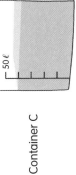

Volume of water = _____ 2 litres _____ or _____ 2 ℓ _____

a Which container holds the greatest volume of water?

Container _____ B _____

b Which container holds the smallest volume of water?

Container _____ D _____

4 Look at the pictures below.
The containers are filled with water.
Which containers hold less than I ℓ of water?
Tick (✓) the answers.

I ℓ {

[ ]

Total volume = I ℓ

[✓]   [✓]

Total volume = I ℓ

[✓]   [✓]   [✓]

5 A paddling pool contains 65 ℓ of water.
Another I5 ℓ of water is added to it.
Later, 40 ℓ are poured out.
What is the volume of water in the paddling pool now?

65 + I5 = 80 ℓ
80 − 40 = 40 ℓ
The volume of water in the paddling pool now is 40 ℓ.

6 Mr Lee buys 27 ℓ of milk in the morning and another 8 ℓ of milk in the evening.
Mr Hall buys 48 ℓ of milk.
a Who buys more milk?
b How much more milk does he buy?

a   27 + 8 = 35 ℓ
Mr Hall buys more milk.

b   48 − 35 = 13 ℓ
Mr Hall buys 13 ℓ more milk than Mr Lee.

7 Mr Thomas uses 10 ℓ of petrol every day.
How much petrol does he use in 7 days?

7 × 10 = 70 ℓ
He uses 70 ℓ of petrol in 7 days.

8 45 ℓ of water is poured into 5 buckets.
Each bucket contains the same volume of water.
What is the volume of water in each bucket?

45 ÷ 5 = 9 ℓ
The volume of water in each bucket is 9 ℓ.

9 A large box contains different types of fruit.
The graph shows the number of each type of fruit in the box.

Number of Types of Fruit in a Box

Apples	○ ○ ○ ○ ○ ○
Oranges	○ ○ ○ ○ ○ ○ ○ ○ ○ ○
Bananas	○ ○ ○ ○
Pears	○ ○ ○
Melons	○ ○ ○ ○

Each ○ stands for 2 pieces of fruit.

Use the graph to answer the following questions.

a There are ___20___ oranges in the box.

b The number of ___melons___ and ___bananas___ in the box are the same.

c There are ___6___ fewer pears than apples.

d There are ___12___ more oranges than bananas.

e There are ___20___ apples and melons altogether.

10 A group of children go to visit a farm.
They are divided into 5 groups.
The number of children in each group is shown in the graph below.

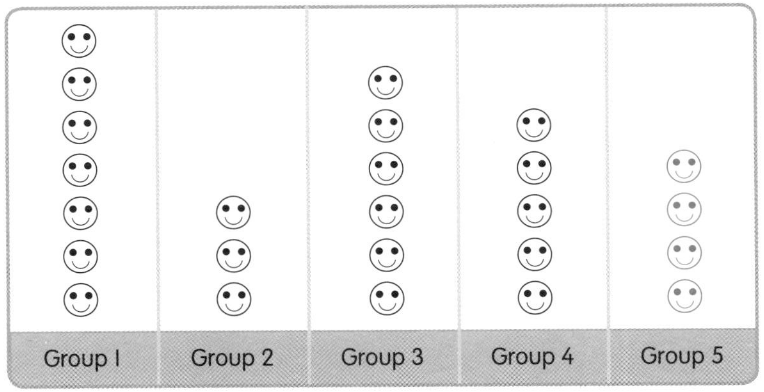

Group 1	Group 2	Group 3	Group 4	Group 5

a There are 15 children in Group 2.
What does each 😊 stand for? _____5 children_____

b How many more children are there in Group 1 than in
Group 4? _____10 children_____

c There are 35 children in Group 3.
How many more 😊 must you draw on the graph?
_____1_____

d How many fewer children are in Group 2 than in Group 4?
_____10 children_____

e Draw 😊 to show 20 children in Group 5.

Review 6

42

Unit 16: Lines and Surfaces

Week	Learning Objectives	Thinking Skills	Resources
4	**(1) Straight lines and curves** Pupils will be able to: • identify and differentiate straight lines and curves • use a ruler and pencil to draw straight lines • use a pencil to draw curves • use 'finger-tracing' to feel and tell whether a line is a curve or a straight line • identify straight lines and curves in pictures and 3D shapes • draw pictures with only straight lines; pictures with only curves or pictures with straight lines and curves *Let's Explore!* Pupils will be able to create pictures with straight lines and curves.	• Comparing • Classifying • Identifying relationships • Visualising	• Pupil Textbook 2B, pp 110 to 114 • Practice Book 2D, pp 43 to 48 • Teacher's Guide 2B, pp 194 to 198

Unit 16: Lines and Surfaces

Week	Learning Objectives	Thinking Skills	Resources
4 – 5	**(2) Flat surfaces** Pupils will be able to: • differentiate between a flat surface and a curved surface by moving their hand over the surfaces • identify 3D objects that have flat surfaces • count the number of flat surfaces of a given set of geometrical shapes • find objects that have flat surfaces	• Comparing • Classifying • Visualising	• Pupil Textbook 2B, pp 115 to 118 • Practice Book 2D, pp 49 to 52 • Teacher's Guide 2B, pp 199 to 202
5	*Put On Your Thinking Caps!* Pupils will be able to: • identify and count the number of curves in pictures • identify objects with curves that match	• Spatial visualisation	• Pupil Textbook 2B, p 119 • Practice Book 2D, p 53 • Teacher's Guide 2B, p 203

Lines and Surfaces

Learning objectives: Straight lines and curves

Pupils will be able to:

- identify and differentiate straight lines and curves
- use a ruler and pencil to draw straight lines
- use a pencil to draw curves
- use 'finger-tracing' to feel and tell whether a line is a curve or a straight line

- identify straight lines and curves in pictures and 3D shapes
- draw pictures with only straight lines; pictures with only curves or pictures with straight lines and curves

Key concepts

- Represent lengths with straight lines
- Interpret straight lines with given lengths

Thinking skills

- Comparing
- Classifying
- Identifying relationships
- Visualising

Teaching sequence

- Show pupils these different straight lines such as those shown on the page in the textbook.
- Rotate the lines to show conservation of straight lines.

- Show pupils these different curves such as those shown on the page in the textbook.
- Rotate the curves to show conservation of curves.

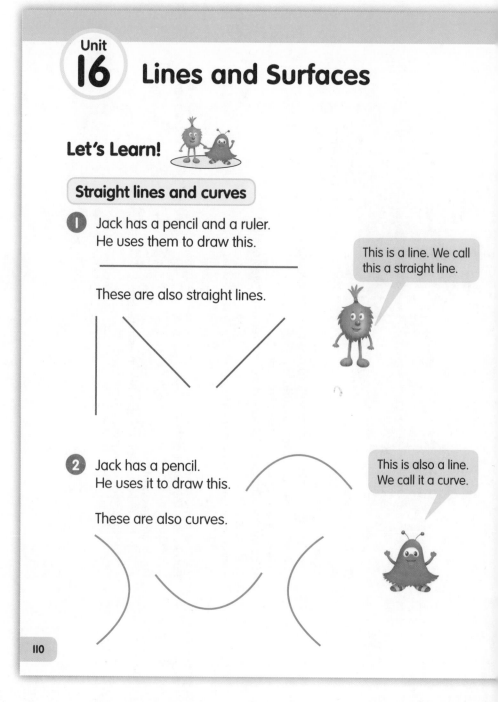

Unit
16 **Lines and Surfaces**

Let's Learn!

| Straight lines and curves |

1 Jack has a pencil and a ruler. He uses them to draw this.

These are also straight lines.

> This is a line. We call this a straight line.

2 Jack has a pencil. He uses it to draw this.

These are also curves.

> This is also a line. We call it a curve.

110

- Point out to pupils that the letters "Y" and "M" have only straight lines and no curves. Ask pupils to think of more letters that are made up of only straight lines.
- Point out to pupils that the letters "C" and "O" have only curves and no straight lines. Ask pupils to think of more letters that are made up of only curves.

Lines and Surfaces **Unit 16**

Teaching sequence

③

- Show pupils the examples of curves, straight lines and pictures made using both straight lines and curves, such as the examples shown on the page in the textbook.

③ Here are more examples of straight lines and curves.

These are more straight lines.

These are more curves.

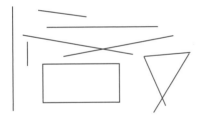

Each of these pictures is made using both straight lines and curves.

Each of these pictures is made using only straight lines or only curves.

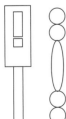
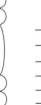

III

Additional activity

Ask pupils to work in groups. Ask each group to draw several straight lines and curves on a large sheet of paper. Swap the drawings between the groups and ask pupils to label the lines 'curves' or 'straight'.

Teaching sequence

- Use this activity to check pupils' understanding of straight lines and curves.

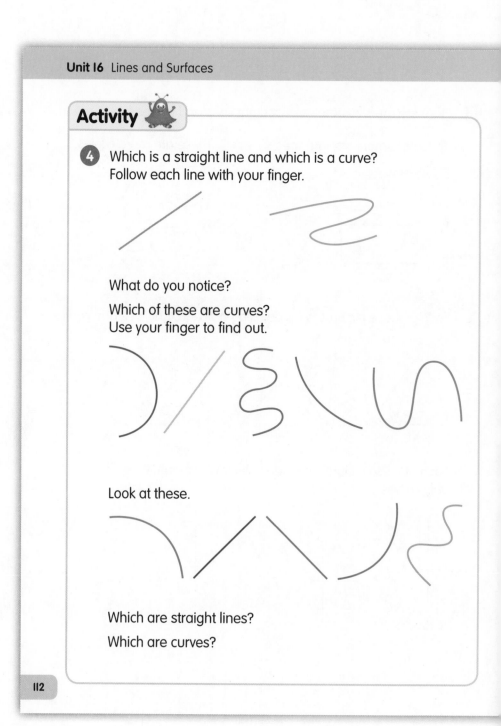

5 Peter made an object with sticks.

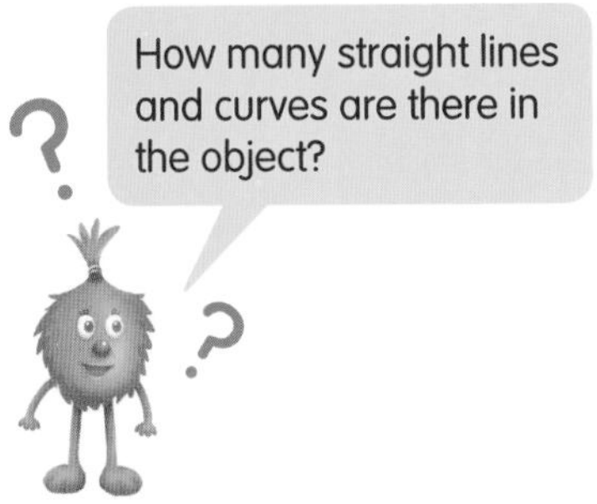

How many straight lines and curves are there in the object?

curve

straight line

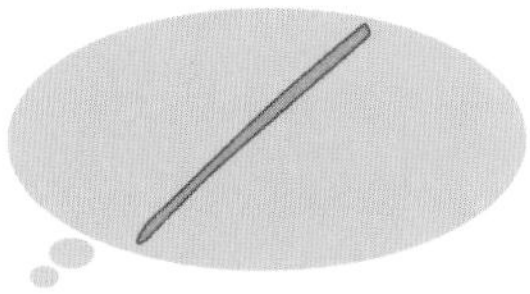

I straight line

I straight line and I curve

6 The shape below is made using straight lines and curves.

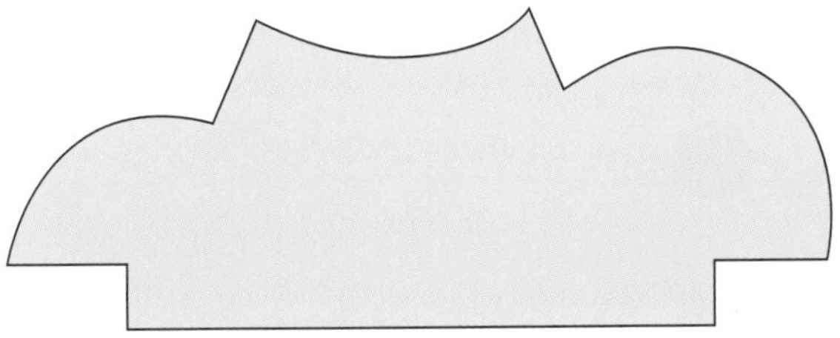

There are ⌐7⌐ straight lines and ⌐3⌐ curves.

5 and **6**

• Use this question to check whether pupils are able to differentiate between straight lines and curves.

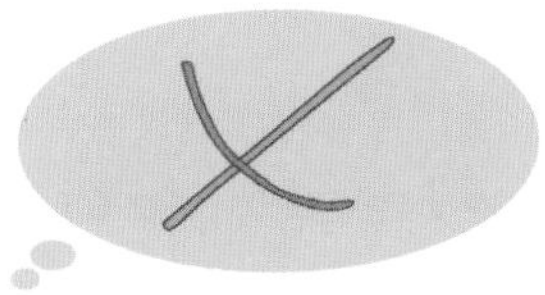

Additional activity

Ask pupils to work in pairs.
Pupil A says two numbers, x and y (each less than 10).

Pupil B draws x different straight lines and y different curves.

Pupil A checks Pupil B's lines. Then they swap roles.

Objective of activity

Pupils will be able to create pictures with straight lines and curves.

Independent work

Practice I and *Maths Journal* in Practice Book 2D, pp 43 to 48.

What you will need

- 3D shapes of a cube, cuboid, cone and cylinder
- I2 drinking straws per pupil

Teaching sequence

- Ask pupils to draw different shapes with different combinations of straight lines and curves.

8

- Prompt pupils to trace the bottom of the shapes and guide them to see the straight lines and curves.
- Ask pupils to identify and mark the outlines they have drawn.
- Ask them to count the number of straight lines and curves.

9 *Let's Explore!*

- Ask pupils to explore the different shapes that can be made by joining different numbers of drinking straws.
- Encourage them to record their findings by drawing the shapes they make and share them with the class.

Unit I6 Lines and Surfaces

7 Ella draws this shape.

It has two straight lines and a curve.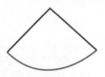

a Draw two shapes that have 2 straight lines and a curve each. Answers vary

b Draw two shapes that have 2 curves and a straight line each. Answers vary

c Draw two shapes with more than 2 straight lines and 2 curves each.
Write down the number of straight lines and curves in each.
Answers vary

Activity

8 You will need the following shapes.

Trace the outline of the bottom of each shape.
What lines do you notice?

Practice Book 2D, p.43

Let's Explore!

9 You will need I2 straws.
Make some shapes with the straws.
Draw the shapes you have made.

a How many straight lines are there in each shape?

b Which shape uses the most straws?

II4

Pupils will be able to:

- differentiate between a flat surface and a curved surface by moving their hand over the surfaces
- identify 3D objects that have flat surfaces
- count the number of flat surfaces of a given set of geometrical shapes
- find objects that have flat surfaces

Thinking skills

- Comparing
- Classifying
- Visualising

Key concept

Identifying flat surfaces and curved surfaces

What you will need

- Table
- Photo

Lines and Surfaces **Unit 16**

Let's Learn!

Flat surfaces

> This table top has a flat surface.

When you move the palm of your hand over a table top, what do you notice?
Does your hand turn?

> The photo has a flat surface.

What other things around you have flat surfaces?

II5

Teaching sequence

①

- Introduce flat surfaces by asking pupils to move their hands over the table top.
- Ask them to take out some objects from their school bag and find out which also have flat surfaces, e.g., books or pencil cases.

Teaching sequence

- Introduce curved surfaces and encourage pupils to touch and slowly move their hands over the surface of a ball.
- Ask them to take out some objects from their school bag and find out which have curved surfaces, e.g., water bottle or glue stick.
- Prompt pupils to name some objects that do not have flat surfaces.
- Ask them to name some objects that have both flat and curved surfaces.

This ball does not have a flat surface.

Move the palm of your hand over the surface of a ball. Does your hand turn?

Does this orange have a flat surface?

What other objects around you do not have flat surfaces?

116

What you will need

- Hardback book
- Bookmark
- Balloon
- Apple
- Photo frame
- Pencil
- Handkerchief
- Marble
- Tissue box
- Glass cup
- Ruler

3 Look at these objects.

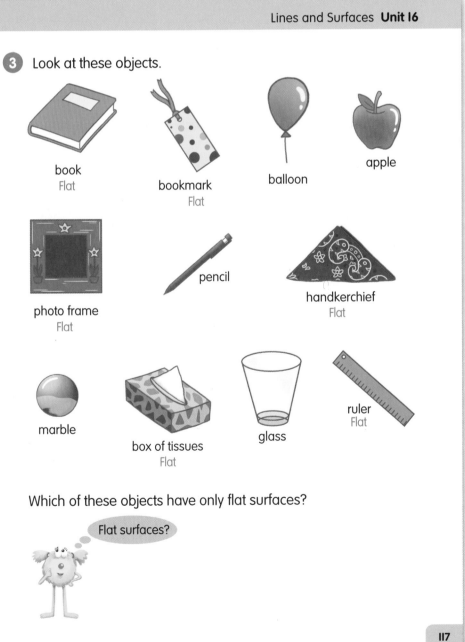

book
Flat

bookmark
Flat

balloon

apple

photo frame
Flat

pencil

handkerchief
Flat

marble

box of tissues
Flat

glass

ruler
Flat

Which of these objects have only flat surfaces?

Flat surfaces?

117

Teaching sequence

3

- Use this activity to check whether pupils can identify flat surfaces.

Teaching sequence

- Ask pupils to work in groups to complete this activity. Use this activity to check whether pupils can identify flat surfaces.

- Encourage pupils to look around the classroom (or the school) to find common objects that have only flat surfaces. Ask them to name the shapes made by the flat surfaces.

- 3D shapes: cube, cuboid, cone, cylinder and square-based pyramid
- Photocopy master 12 (see p 261)

Practice 2 in Practice Book 2D, pp 49 to 52.

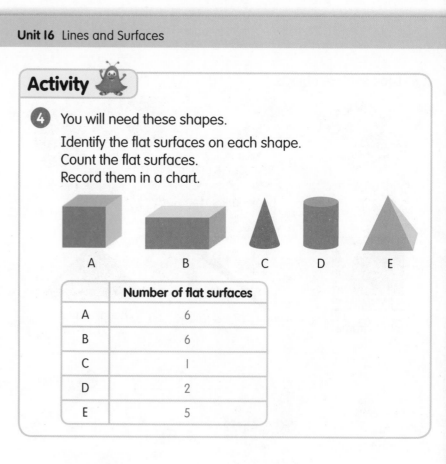

Unit 16 Lines and Surfaces

Activity

4 You will need these shapes.

Identify the flat surfaces on each shape.
Count the flat surfaces.
Record them in a chart.

A   B   C   D   E

	Number of flat surfaces
A	6
B	6
C	1
D	2
E	5

Activity

5 Find two objects that have only flat surfaces.
You can look around the classroom or use a computer to find pictures of them.

Identify the shape on the flat surface.
Draw or print the pictures.

Practice Book 2D, p.49

118

Lines and Surfaces **Unit 16**

Put On Your Thinking Caps!

6 **a** Look at the picture below.
How many straight lines and curves are needed to make it? 1 straight line, 8 curves

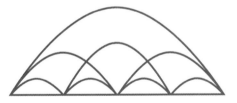

b A piece of paper was cut up into 3 pieces.

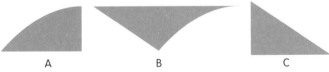

A   B   C

Trace and cut out these 3 shapes.
Rearrange them to make a triangle.

c Trace and cut out the following shapes to make a square.

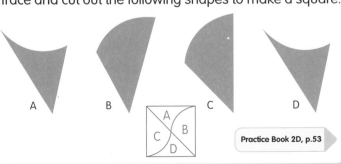

A   B   C   D

Practice Book 2D, p.53

119

Teaching sequence

6 *Put On Your Thinking Caps!*

a

- If necessary, show pupils the diagram shown on the page in the textbook and point as you count the number of curves and straight lines.
- Point out that there is only one straight line, not 4 (along the bottom of the diagram).

b and **c**

- Ask pupils to work in groups to solve these puzzles.
- Invite volunteers to present their solution to the rest of the class.

Unit 16 Lines and Surfaces

Date: _____

Practice 1 Straight lines and curves

1 Look at these pictures.

Draw the pictures in the correct space in the table below.

Straight lines only	
Curves only	
Straight lines and curves	

3 Hardeep draws some pictures with straight lines and curves. Count the number of straight lines and curves he uses.

a

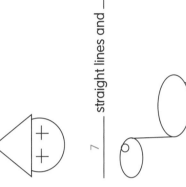

_7_ straight lines and _1_ curve.

b

_3_ straight lines and _3_ curves.

c

_3_ straight lines and _32_ curves.

---

2 Look at these letters.

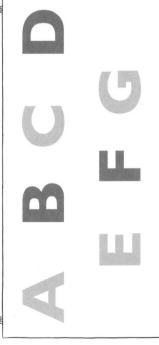

A B C D
E F G

Which of these letters have

a straight lines only? _A, E, F_

b curves only? _C_

c straight lines and curves? _B, D, G_

Draw three other letters using straight lines only.

Answers vary

Draw three other letters using straight lines and curves.

Answers vary

206 **Answers Unit 16:** Lines and Surfaces

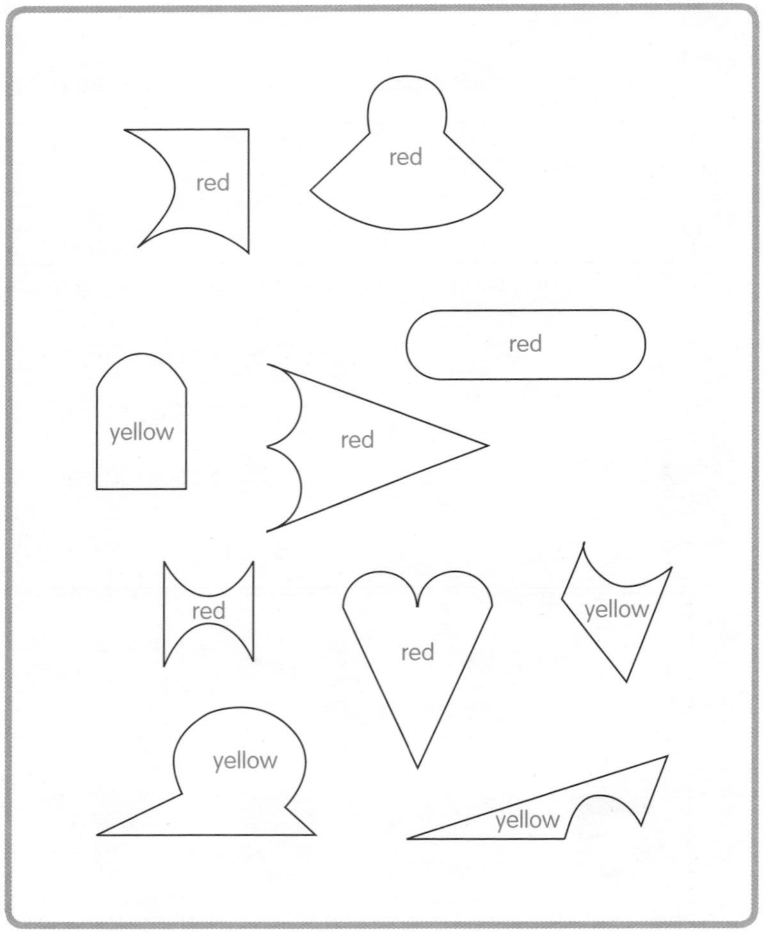

5 Draw a picture in each box.
Use the correct number of straight lines and curves.

a more than 5 straight lines

Answers vary

b fewer than 8 curves

Answers vary

c more than 10 straight lines and curves

Answers vary

4 Colour the shapes with 2 straight lines and 2 curved lines in red.
Colour the shapes with 3 straight lines and 1 curved line in yellow.

Practice 2 Flat surfaces

1 Fill in the spaces.

a 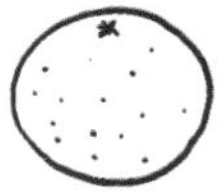
The orange has ___0___ flat surfaces.

b 
The tin has ___2___ flat surfaces.

c 
The vase has ___1___ flat surface.

d 
The cereal box has ___6___ flat surfaces.

Date: _____

49

Unit 16: Lines and Surfaces

Maths Journal

Date: _____

1 Draw a happy face using curves only. *Answers vary*

Draw a sad face using straight lines and curves. *Answers vary*

48

Unit 16: Lines and Surfaces

Answers Unit 16: Lines and Surfaces   **207**

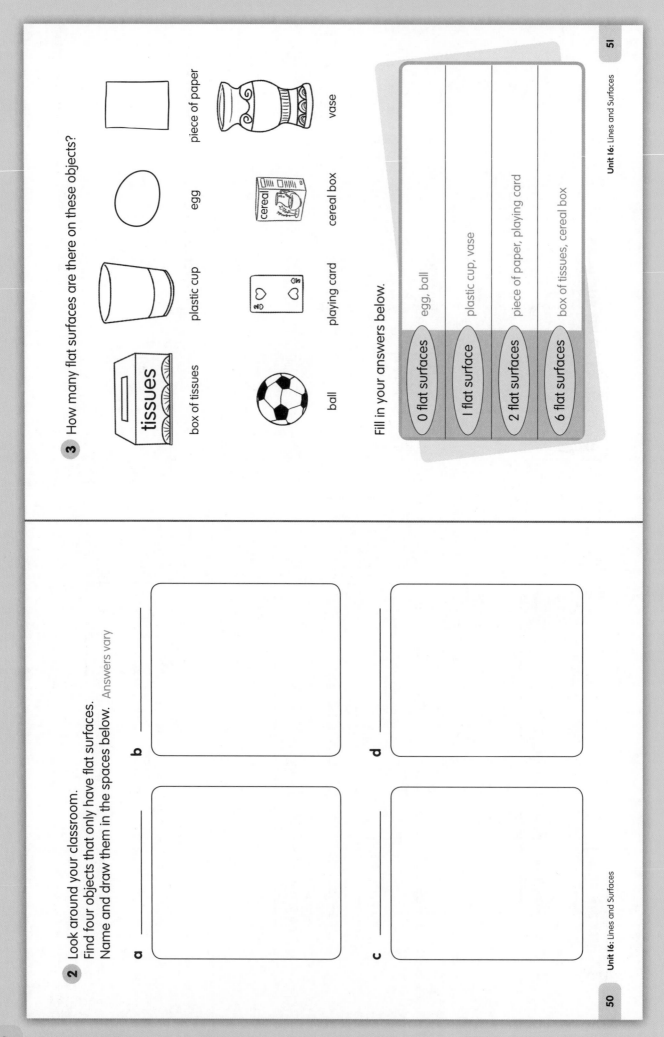

3 How many flat surfaces are there on these objects?

box of tissues

plastic cup

egg

piece of paper

tissues

ball

playing card

cereal box

vase

Fill in your answers below.

0 flat surfaces	egg, ball
1 flat surface	plastic cup, vase
2 flat surfaces	piece of paper, playing card
6 flat surfaces	box of tissues, cereal box

2 Look around your classroom.
Find four objects that only have flat surfaces.
Name and draw them in the spaces below. *Answers vary*

a

b

c

d

Challenging Practice

1 Cut out the shapes below and stick them onto a piece of paper to make a square.

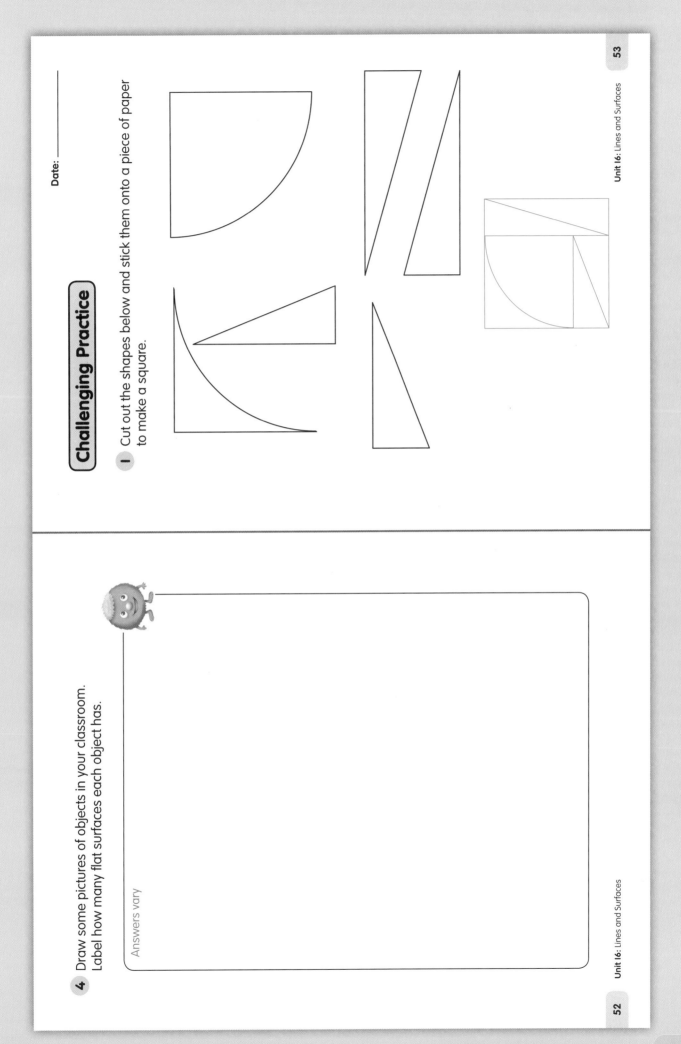

4 Draw some pictures of objects in your classroom. Label how many flat surfaces each object has.

Answers vary

Unit 17: Shapes and Patterns

Week	Learning Objectives	Thinking Skills	Resources
5 – 6	**(1) 2D shapes** Pupils will be able to: • recognise a semicircle as half a circle and a quarter circle as one quarter of a circle • recognise things with semicircular shapes and things with quarter circle shapes • recognise semicircles and quarter circles in composite shapes • make pictures using shapes including semicircles and quarter circles • make pictures from cut-out shapes • draw shapes • copy shapes onto square dotty paper • copy shapes onto squared paper	• Visualising shapes	• Pupil Textbook 2B, pp 120 to 128 • Practice Book 2D, pp 55 to 66 • Teacher's Guide 2B, pp 212 to 220
6	**(2) 3D shapes** Pupils will be able to: • recognise, identify and name the 3D shapes: cube, cuboid, cone and cylinder • identify and name the 3D shapes used in making a given model • make models using the 3D shapes	• Visualising shapes	• Pupil Textbook 2B, pp 129 to 131 • Practice Book 2D, pp 67 to 68 • Teacher's Guide 2B, pp 221 to 223

Unit 17: Shapes and Patterns

Medium-term plan

Week	Learning Objectives	Thinking Skills	Resources
6	**(3) Making patterns** Pupils will be able to: • identify patterns using the attributes: size, shape, colour and orientation • identify shapes in repeating sequences • identify missing shapes from patterns • explain a pattern and continue the pattern • make simple repeating patterns using 1 or 2 attributes and explain how they made the pattern • make new patterns with the given basic shapes	• Classifying • Comparing • Identifying patterns and shapes • Spatial visualisation	• Pupil Textbook 2B, pp 132 to 135 • Practice Book 2D, pp 69 to 71 • Teacher's Guide 2B, pp 224 to 227
6	*Put On Your Thinking Caps!* Pupils will be able to use tangram pieces to make a square. Revision 2	• Comparing • Spatial visualisation	• Pupil Textbook 2B, p 136 • Practice Book 2D, pp 73 to 74 • Teacher's Guide 2B, p 228 • Practice Book 2D, pp 75 to 88

Summative assessment opportunities

Assessment Book 2, Test 8, pp 93 to 100
For extension, Assessment Book 2, Challenging Problems 4, pp 101 to 102
Assessment Book 2, Check-up 4, pp 103 to 116

Shapes and Patterns

Pupils will be able to:

- recognise a semicircle as half a circle and a quarter circle as one quarter of a circle
- recognise things with semicircular shapes and things with quarter circle shapes

- recognise semicircles and quarter circles in composite shapes
- make pictures using shapes including semicircles and quarter circles
- make pictures from cut-out shapes
- draw shapes
- copy shapes onto square dotty paper

- copy shapes onto squared paper

Key concept

Identifying semicircles and quarter circles

Thinking skill

Visualising shapes

Teaching sequence

- As a class, revise what a circle looks like.
- Introduce the shape of a semicircle by showing the diagram of the centre circle on the football field with a semicircle marked in red.
- Alternatively, you could show a circular piece of paper, then fold and cut it into half. Point out that the two halves are semicircles.

Unit
17 Shapes and Patterns

Let's Learn!

2D shapes

1 The children are playing football.

The centre circle is made up of 2 equal halves of a circle. Each half circle is called a **semicircle**.

Each part is $\frac{1}{2}$ of a circle.
Semi means half.

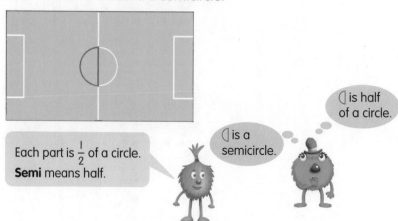

(is a semicircle.

(is half of a circle.

120

Additional activity

As a class, walk around the school's football pitch or netball court. Ask pupils to look out for different shapes. Back in class, show a picture or diagram of a football pitch. Talk about the shapes. The centre circle is made up of 2 equal halves of a circle. Each half is called a semicircle.

What you will need

Photocopy master 15 (see p 264)

2 Farha is playing with her toy car.

Each wheel is made up of 4 equal parts.
Each part is called a **quarter circle**.

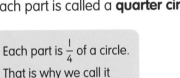

Each part is $\frac{1}{4}$ of a circle.
That is why we call it a quarter circle.

 is a quarter circle.

 is $\frac{1}{4}$ of a circle.

3 Look around the classroom.

Which objects have a semicircle?

Which objects have a quarter circle?

 Home Maths Look for circular food and objects when you are out shopping and ask your child if they can spot any semicircles or quarter circles.

121

Teaching sequence

2

- Encourage pupils to look at the wheels of the toy car and point out that each wheel is made up of 4 equal parts.
- Each part is called a quarter circle because it is a quarter of a circle.
- Alternatively, you could show a circular piece of paper, then fold and cut it into 4 equal parts. Point out that each segment is a quarter.

3

- Use this question to check whether pupils can identify semicircles or quarter circles in shapes around them.

Ask pupils to work in pairs.
Pupil A draws a figure that is
made up of two different basic
shapes, including a quarter
circle. Pupil B identifies the two
shapes that make up the figure
by drawing out the two shapes
separately.

Pupil A and B swap roles and
repeat the activity.

What you will need

Photocopy masters 16 and 17
(see pp 265 and 266)

Teaching sequence

- Guide pupils in carrying out
  this activity.

5

- Check whether pupils can
  identify the semicircle and
  quarter circle shapes.

6

- Show and point out to pupils
  some examples of composite
  pictures made up of the
  basic shapes (semicircle,
  quarter circle, circle, square,
  rectangle, triangle).

Unit I7 Shapes and Patterns

Activity

4 **a** Trace this circle on a piece of paper.
Cut it out.

b Fold the circle into equal halves.
Cut the circle along the fold.
Do you get two semicircles?

c Fold one of the semicircles into equal halves.
Cut the semicircle along the fold.
Do you get two quarter circles?

How many quarter circles can you get from one circle?

5 Look at the shapes below.

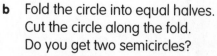

A   B   C   D   E

Which is a semicircle?   C
Which is a quarter circle?   D

6 This picture is made up of three shapes.

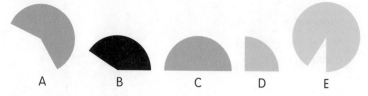

The three shapes are a rectangle, a semicircle and
a quarter circle.

122

What you will need
Photocopy masters 18 and 19
(see pp 267 and 268)

Shapes and Patterns **Unit 17**

Activity

7 a What shapes make up this picture?
Trace the picture on a piece of paper.
Draw lines on your picture to show
the different shapes.

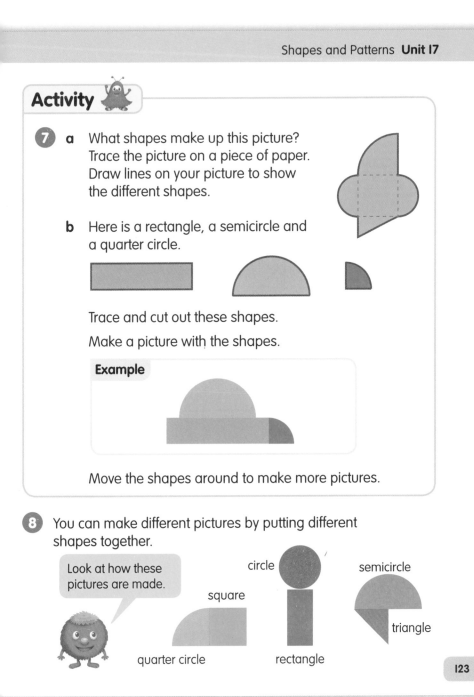

b Here is a rectangle, a semicircle and
a quarter circle.

Trace and cut out these shapes.

Make a picture with the shapes.

Example

Move the shapes around to make more pictures.

8 You can make different pictures by putting different
shapes together.

Look at how these
pictures are made.

circle

square

quarter circle

rectangle

semicircle

triangle

123

Teaching sequence

7

a
- Use this question to assess
pupils informally on their
ability to identify basic shapes
that make up a composite
picture without individual
outlines.

b
- Point out that this activity is the
reverse of **6** and **7 a**.
- Prompt pupils to note that they
can form different composite
pictures using the same basic
shapes.

8
- Encourage pupils to use
cut-outs to make the pictures
shown.

What you will need
Photocopy masters 20 and 2I
(see pp 269 and 270)

Teaching sequence

- Use this activity to check whether pupils can identify the basic shapes that make up each composite picture, given only the outline.

- Use the second question to check whether pupils are able to make composite pictures using the number of shapes specified.

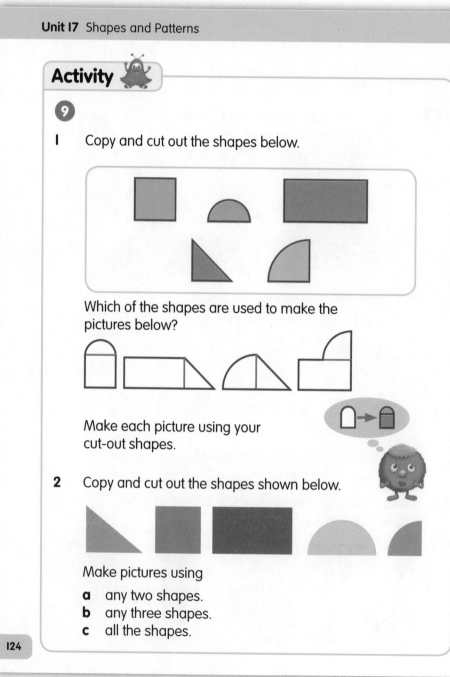

10 The picture below is made up of different shapes.
Name the shapes that make up this picture. semicircles, quarter
circles, square, triangle

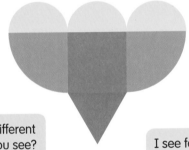

How many different
shapes do you see?

I see four different
shapes!

Activity

11 Draw a picture using shapes.
Use at least four shapes.

Colour in the shapes in your
picture and show it to
your friends!

125

Teaching sequence

10

- Guide pupils to see the four
  different shapes that make up
  the composite picture.

11

- Help pupils to draw pictures
  using at least four shapes.

Square dotty paper
(see Photocopy master 22 on
p 271) or geoboards

Teaching sequence

12 and **13**

- Show an example of how to draw one of the shapes on square dotty paper.
- Then provide pupils with square dotty paper so that they can copy the other shapes.

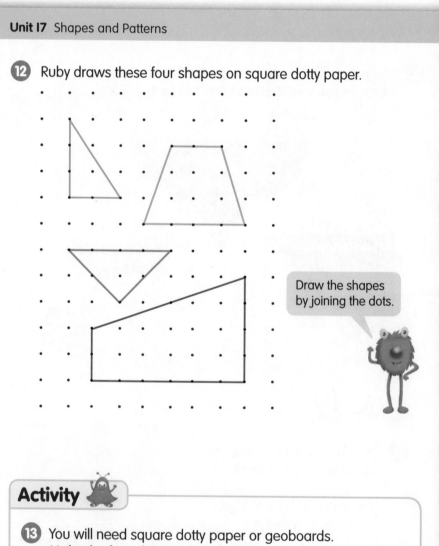

Unit 17 Shapes and Patterns

12 Ruby draws these four shapes on square dotty paper.

Draw the shapes by joining the dots.

Activity

13 You will need square dotty paper or geoboards.
Make the four shapes shown above.

126

What you will need

Squared paper (see Photocopy
master 23 on p 272)

Shapes and Patterns **Unit 17**

14 Peter draws these four shapes on squared paper.

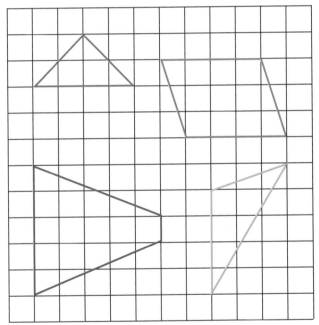

Draw lines to
make the shapes.

Activity

15 You will need squared paper.
Draw the four shapes shown above on the squared paper.

127

Teaching sequence

14 and **15**

- Show an example of how to draw one of the shapes on squared paper.

- Then provide pupils with squared paper so they can copy the other shapes.

What you will need

Square dotty paper and squared paper (see Photocopy masters 22 and 23 on pp 271 and 272)

Independent work

Practice I in Practice Book 2D, pp 55 to 66.

Teaching sequence

16 and **17**

- Provide pupils with square dotty and squared paper and help them copy the shapes.

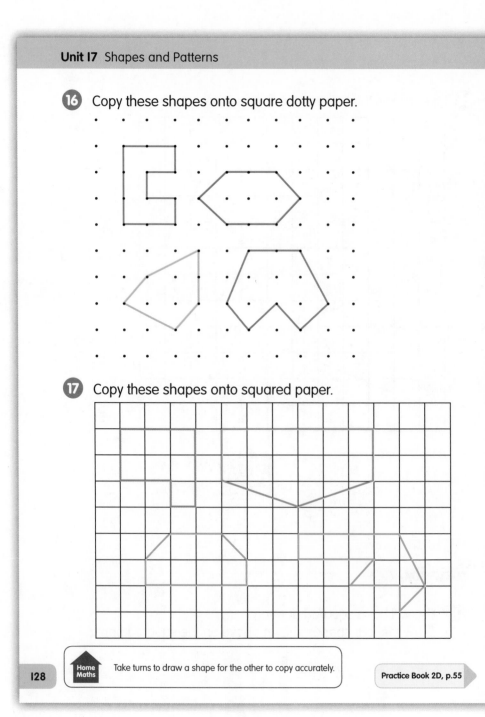

16 Copy these shapes onto square dotty paper.

17 Copy these shapes onto squared paper.

Home Maths   Take turns to draw a shape for the other to copy accurately.

128

Practice Book 2D, p.55

Pupils will be able to:

- recognise, identify and name the 3D shapes: cube, cuboid, cone and cylinder
- identify and name the 3D shapes used in making a given model
- make models using the 3D shapes

Shapes can be visualised as 3D shapes.

Visualising shapes

3D shapes: cube, cuboid, cone, cylinder.

Shapes and Patterns **Unit 17**

Let's Learn!

3D shapes

1 These are some shapes.

cube   cuboid   cone cylinder

I can make a model using a cube and a cuboid.

I can also make a model using a cylinder and a cone.

129

Teaching sequence

1

- Show pupils the 3D shapes – cube, cuboid, cone and cylinder.
- Help them to identify and differentiate the 4 shapes by comparing the similarities and differences.
  E.g. cubes and cuboids have flat faces whereas cones and cylinders have both curved and flat faces.
- Show and explain that composite models can be made using any two of these 4 basic shapes.

Ask pupils to work in small groups.

Give each group four different 3D shapes. Encourage pupils to make different models using these 3D shapes.

Teaching sequence

- Use the question to check whether pupils can identify which 3D shapes make up each composite model.

Unit 17 Shapes and Patterns

2 Look at these models.

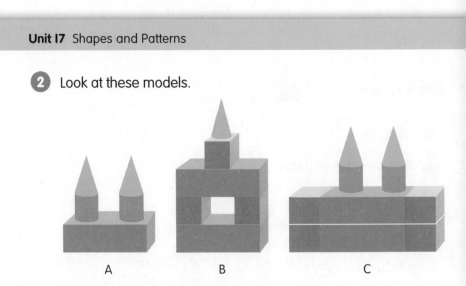

A   B   C

Which shapes make up the models?

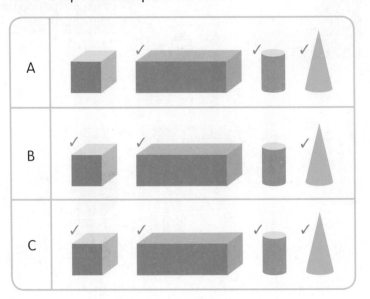

130

Shapes and Patterns **Unit 17**

3 The model below is made up of some shapes.
Count the number of each shape that make up this model.

	How many?
	6
	1
	2
	2

Activity

4 You will need the shapes shown below.

Make a model using

a any four shapes

b at least two shapes of each type

Practice Book 2D, p.67

131

Teaching sequence

3

- Check pupils' understanding by asking them to identify how many of each basic shape make up the composite model.

4

- Ask each pupil to make a composite model using a set of the shapes provided.

Learning objectives: Making patterns

Pupils will be able to:

- identify patterns using the attributes: size, shape, colour and orientation
- identify shapes in repeating sequences
- identify missing shapes from patterns
- explain a pattern and continue the pattern
- make simple repeating patterns using 1 or 2 attributes and explain how they made the pattern

- make new patterns with the given basic shapes

Key concepts

Patterns are made by repeating sequences.

Thinking skills

- Classifying
- Comparing
- Identifying patterns and shapes
- Spatial visualisation

Teaching sequence

- For the patterns shown, point out to pupils the change in:
  a size
  b shape

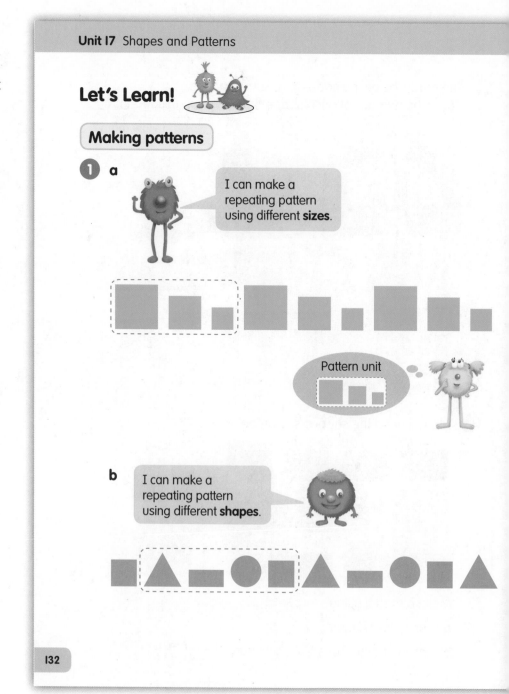

c

I can make a repeating pattern using different **colours**.

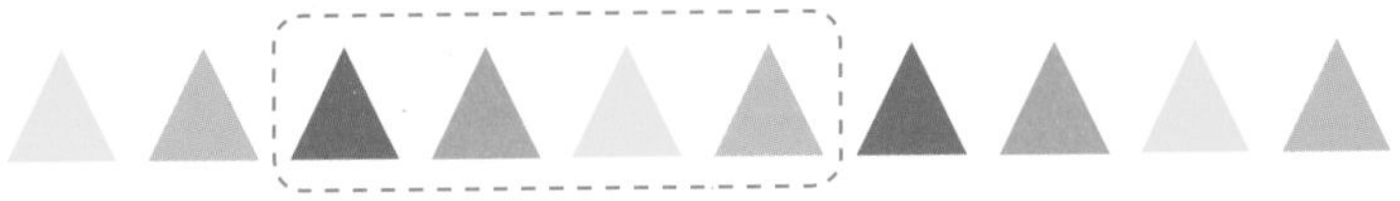

d

I can make a repeating pattern by turning the shapes.

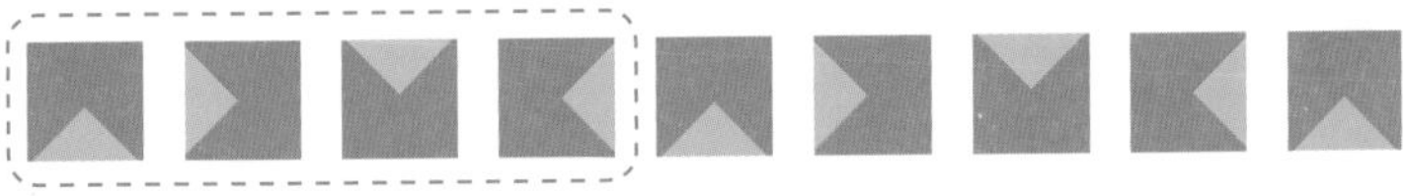

2 I can make a repeating pattern using **two different sizes and shapes**.

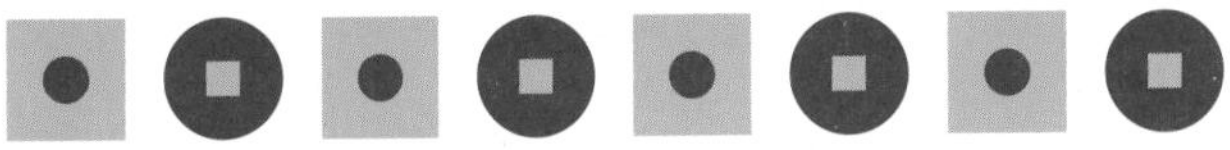

? ?

Explain the pattern.
Then continue the pattern.

133

- For the patterns shown, point out to pupils the change in:
  c colour
  d orientation

2

- Prompt pupils to see that there are two basic shapes, and that the pattern is made by alternating them.

- Ask pupils to draw the next two shapes in the pattern.

Encourage pupils to draw other repeated patterns using basic shapes.

Teaching sequence

- Explain to pupils that there are two attributes involved in making these patterns.
- Ask pupils to point out the repeated sequences and how the pattern changes.

- Assess pupils informally to check whether they are able to identify the repeated sequences and provide the next two shapes in the pattern.

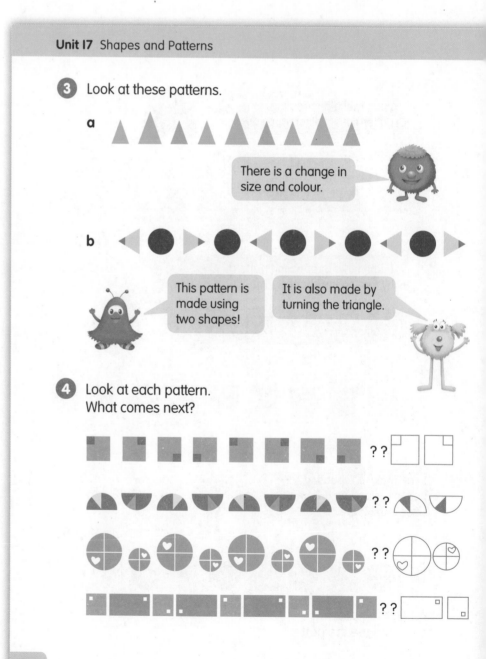

- Cut-outs of the shapes (see Photocopy master 24 on p 273)
- Art paper
- Strips of paper
- Clothes hangers
- String

Independent work

Practice 3 and *Maths Journal* in Practice Book 2D, pp 69 to 72.

Teaching sequence

5

- Encourage pupils to follow the steps to make patterns using the cut-outs.

Shapes and Patterns **Unit 17**

Activity

5 **Pattern mobile!**

You will need cut-outs of the following shapes, art paper, string, three strips of plain paper, and a clothes hanger.

1 Draw round the cut-outs.

2 Colour and cut out the shapes.

3 Arrange the cut-outs to make three different patterns.

4 Stick the patterns on the strips of plain paper.

5 Tie the three strips of paper to the clothes hanger.

6 Now you have your own pattern mobile!

Practice Book 2D, p.69

135

Objective of activity

Pupils will be able to use tangram pieces to make a square.

Thinking skills

- Comparing
- Spatial visualisation

What you will need

Tangram (see Photocopy master 25 on p 274)

Independent work

Challenging Practice and Revision 2 in Practice Book 2D, pp 73 to 88.

Teaching sequence

6 *Put On Your Thinking Caps!*

- Ask pupils to cut out the pieces of the tangram.
- Help them to recognise the layout of the individual pieces in the tangram.
- Mix up the pieces and challenge pupils to put the tangram back together.

Put On Your Thinking Caps!

6 This is a tangram.
It is a square made up of seven pieces of different shapes.

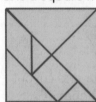

You will need a copy of this tangram on a piece of coloured paper. Cut along its lines like this:

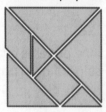

Now mix up the pieces.

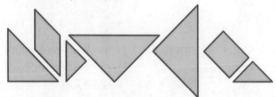

Put them back into the shape of a square.
How many minutes did you take?
Were you faster than your friends?

Practice Book 2D, p.73

136

Unit 17 Shapes and Patterns

Practice 1 **2D shapes**

1 Draw round a plastic circle on a piece of paper.
Cut out the circle.
Fold the circle into equal halves.
Cut it along the fold.
Draw these new shapes in the box below.

These are called ___semicircles___ .

2 Draw round a plastic circle on a piece of paper.
Cut out the circle.
Fold the circle into 4 equal parts.
Cut it along the folds.
Draw these new shapes in the box below.

These are called ___quarter circles___ .

Unit 17: Shapes and Patterns

55

4 Draw a picture using only semicircles and quarter circles.

Answers vary

3 Look at the shapes below.
Colour the semicircles red and the quarter circles yellow.

yellow

red

yellow

red

yellow

yellow

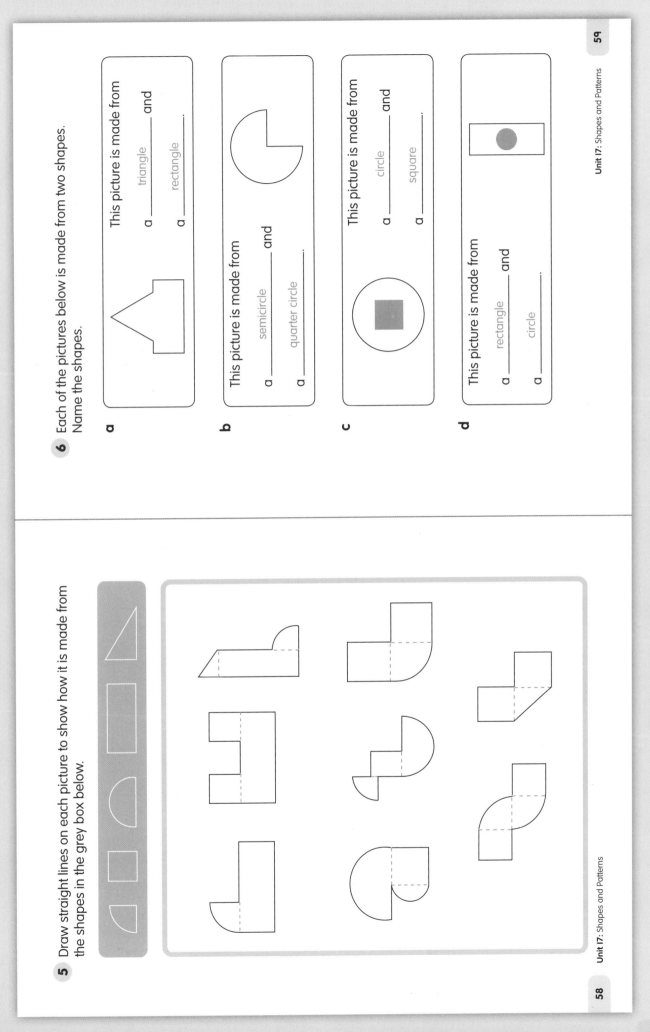

5 Draw straight lines on each picture to show how it is made from the shapes in the grey box below.

6 Each of the pictures below is made from two shapes. Name the shapes.

a This picture is made from

a _triangle_ and

a _rectangle_ .

b This picture is made from

a _semicircle_ and

a _quarter circle_ .

c This picture is made from

a _circle_ and

a _square_ .

d This picture is made from

a _rectangle_ and

a _circle_ .

7 Colour the missing piece in each box to complete each shape.

a

A square

b

A circle

c

A rectangle

d

A rectangle

8 Cut out the shapes on the right.
Use the shapes to make each picture on the left.
Glue your pictures onto a piece of paper.

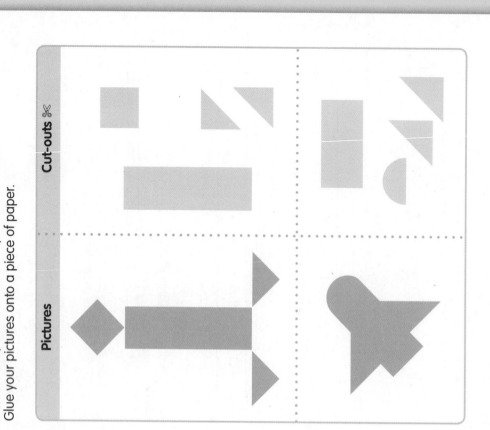

Pictures	Cut-outs ✂

Cut-outs ✂

Pictures

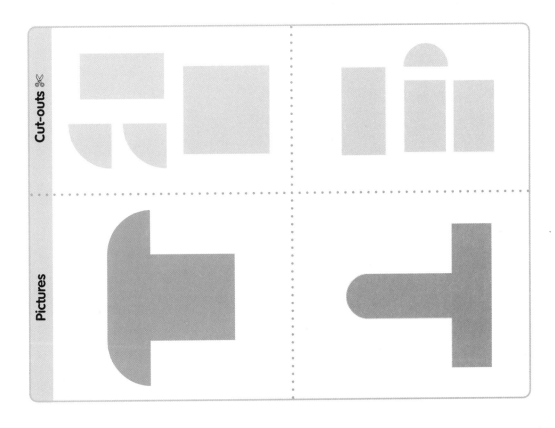

9 Copy these shapes onto the square dotty paper on the right.

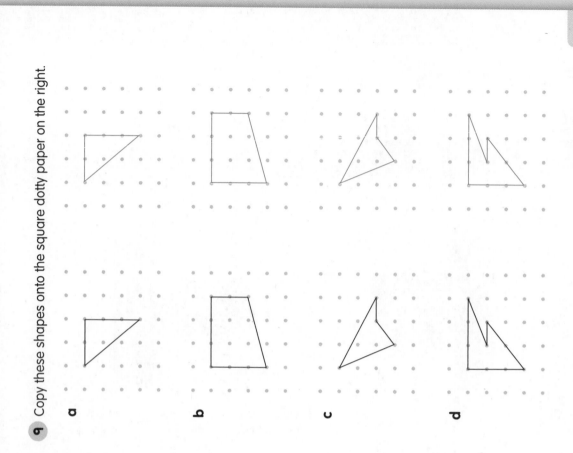

a

b

c

d

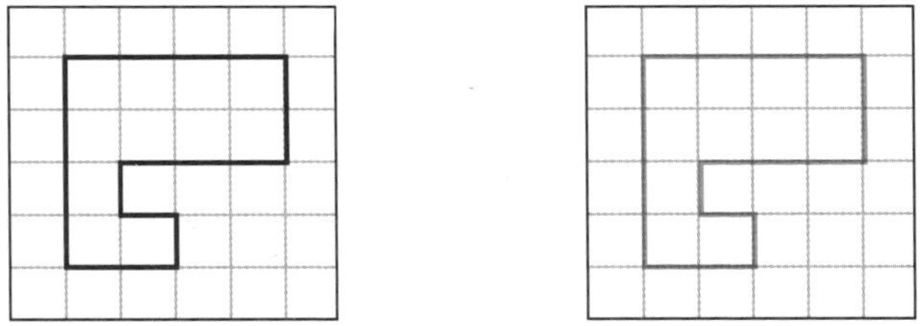

Practice 2 · 3D shapes

1 a Write down the number of each shape used in the models.

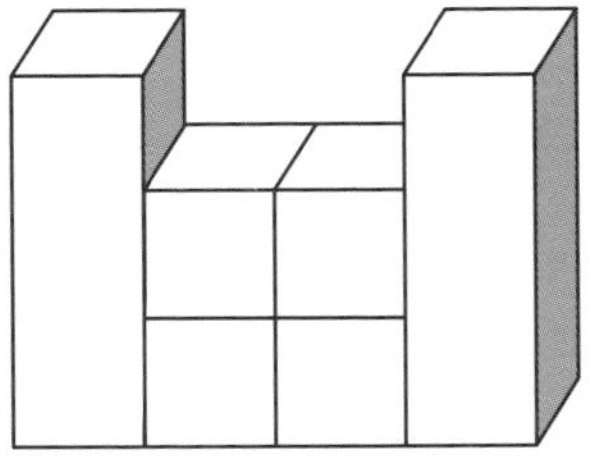

Shape	A	B
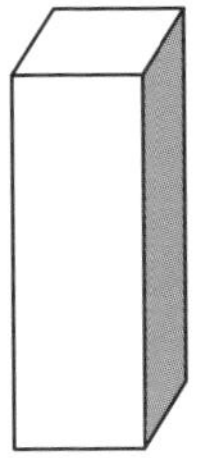 Cuboid	2	2
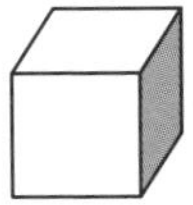 Cube	4	2
 Cone	0	2
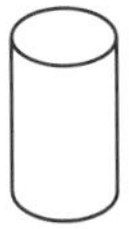 Cylinder	0	2

A

B

10 Copy these shapes onto the squared paper on the right.

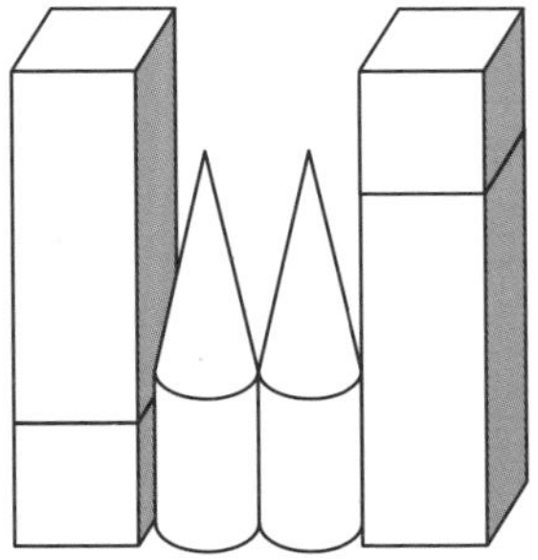

a

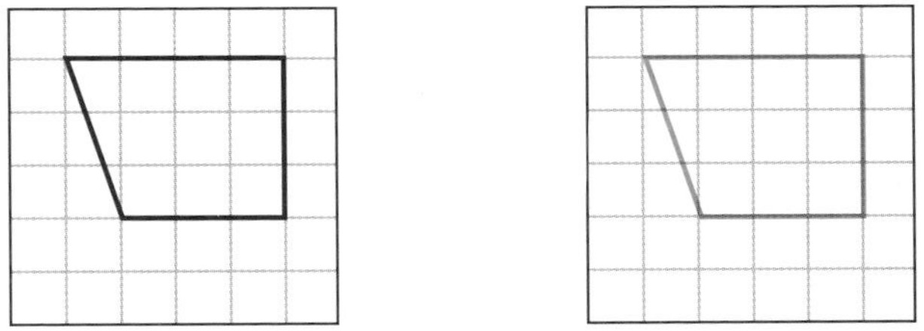

b

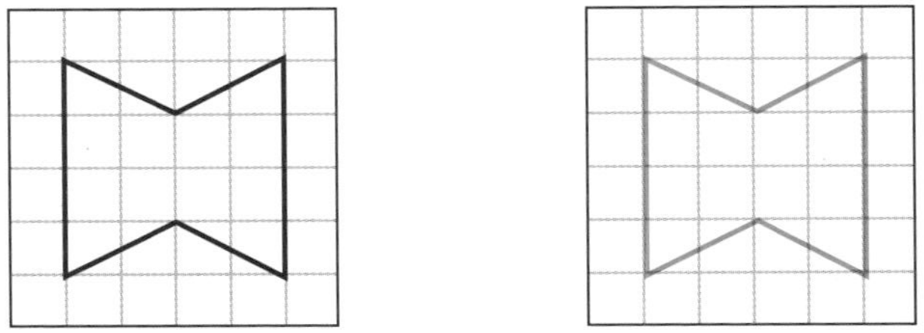

c

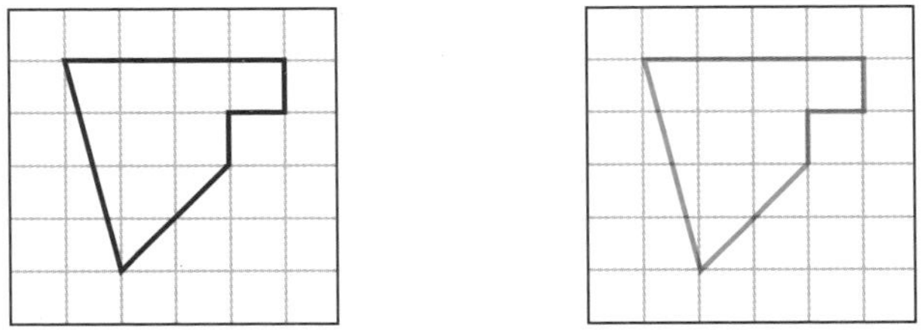

d

Practice 3   Making patterns

1 Look at the patterns.
What comes next?

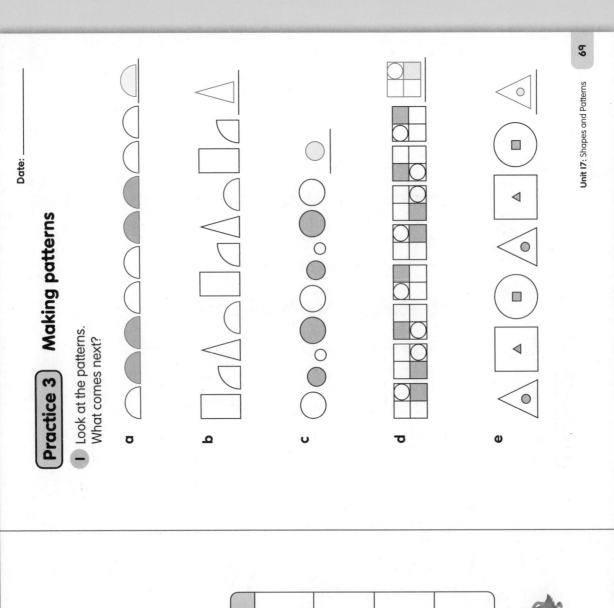

a

b

c

d

e

b

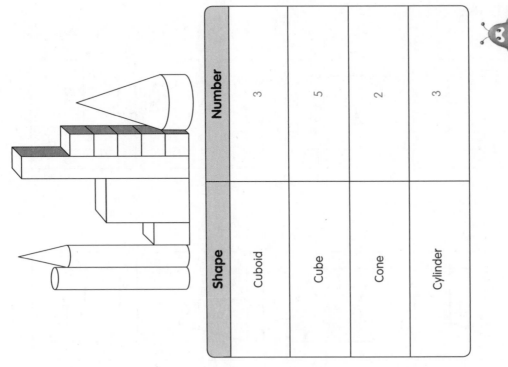

Shape	Number
Cuboid	3
Cube	5
Cone	2
Cylinder	3

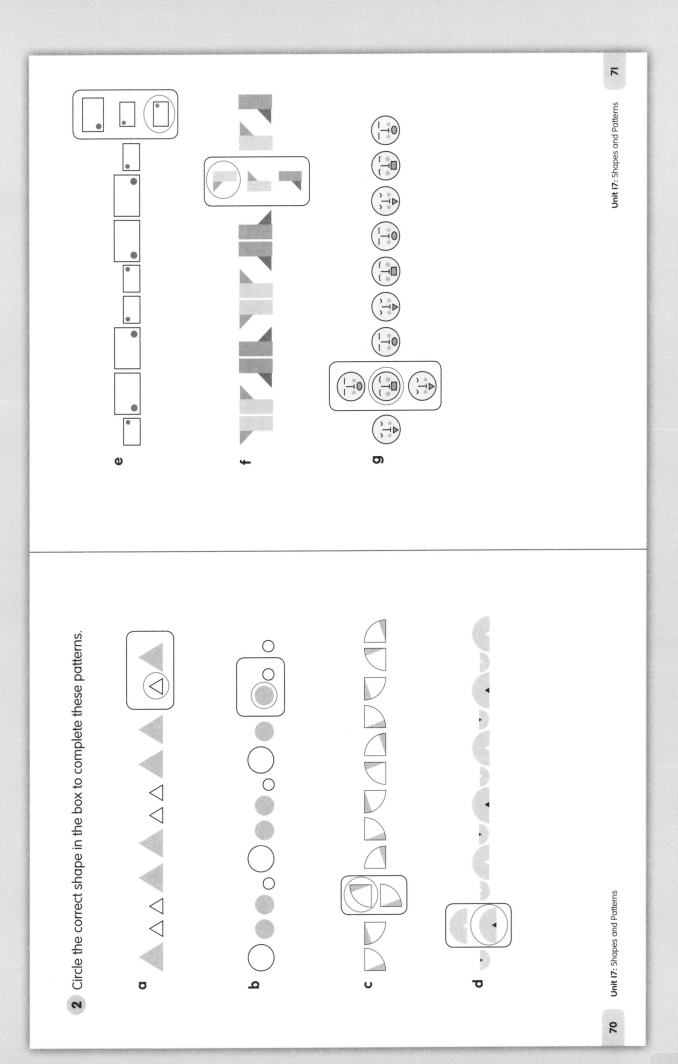

2 Circle the correct shape in the box to complete these patterns.

a

b

c

d

e

f

g

Maths Journal

Date: _____

1 Miya makes a pattern using some shapes.
   Circle the shape that is wrong.
   Then draw the correct shape.

◻ ○ ◻ ○ ◻ ⟨▷⟩ ○

The correct shape is

☐

Jack makes another pattern using some shapes.
Circle the shape that is wrong.
Then draw the correct shape.

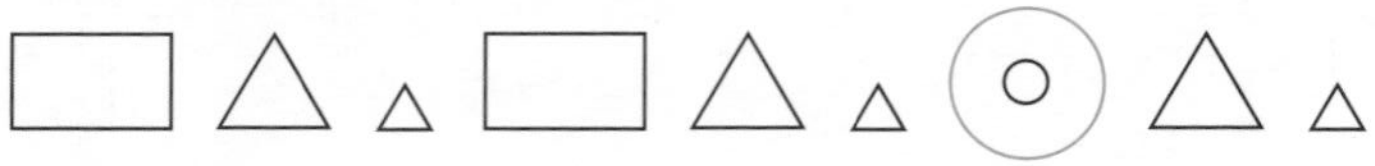

◻ △ ◻ △ ◻ △ ⟨○⟩ △ △

The correct shape is

☐

Challenging Practice

Date: _____

1 Use the 2D shapes you know to make a pattern in each box.

a Use different types of shapes.

Answers vary

b Use different sizes of one shape.

Answers vary

Revision 2

Date: _____

Section A
Choose the correct answer.
Write its letter in the box.

1. 561 + 39 = _____

   a 590   b 599
   c 600   d 699

   [c]

2. Which of the following is correct?

   a In 345, the digit 3 is in the ones place.
   b In 345, the digit 5 is in the ones place.
   c In 345, the digit 5 is in the tens place.
   d In 345, the digit 4 is in the hundreds place.

   [b]

3. 24 divided by 4 is _____.

   a 3   b 4
   c 5   d 6

   [d]

4. 500 + 40 + 3 = _____

   a 345   b 354
   c 435   d 543

   [d]

---

c Use different colours of one shape.

Answers vary

d Make a pattern by turning one shape.

Answers vary

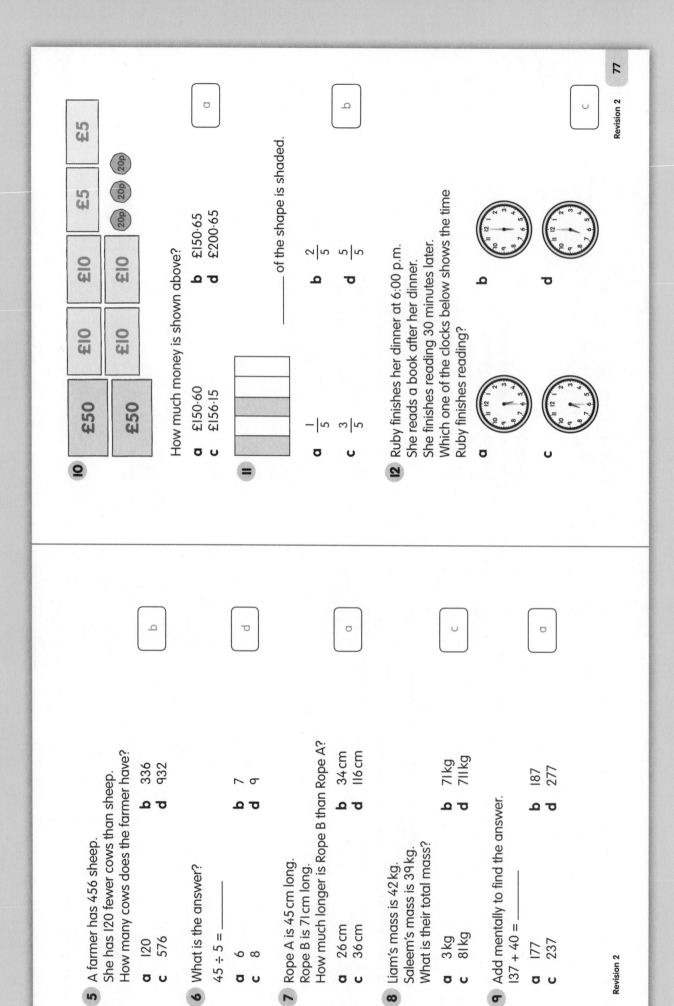

5 A farmer has 456 sheep.
She has 120 fewer cows than sheep.
How many cows does the farmer have?

a 120   b 336
c 576   d 932

b

6 What is the answer?

45 ÷ 5 = _____

a 6   b 7
c 8   d 9

d

7 Rope A is 45 cm long.
Rope B is 71 cm long.
How much longer is Rope B than Rope A?

a 26 cm   b 34 cm
c 36 cm   d 116 cm

a

8 Liam's mass is 42 kg.
Saleem's mass is 39 kg.
What is their total mass?

a 3 kg   b 71 kg
c 81 kg   d 711 kg

c

9 Add mentally to find the answer.

137 + 40 = _____

a 177   b 187
c 237   d 277

a

10 £50 £50 £10 £10 £10 £10 £5 £5 20p 20p 20p

How much money is shown above?

a £150·60   b £150·65
c £156·15   d £200·65

a

11 _____ of the shape is shaded.

a $\frac{1}{5}$ b $\frac{2}{5}$
c $\frac{3}{5}$ d $\frac{5}{5}$

b

12 Ruby finishes her dinner at 6:00 p.m.
She reads a book after her dinner.
She finishes reading 30 minutes later.
Which one of the clocks below shows the time
Ruby finishes reading?

a   b

c   d

c

17 Mr Khan pours some cups of water into two buckets,
A and B.

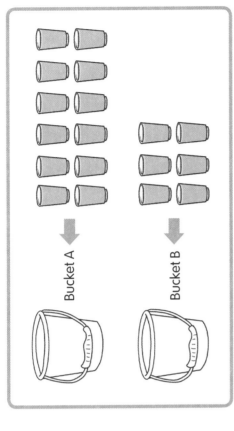

Bucket A

Bucket B

How many more cups of water should he pour into Bucket B
so that it has the same amount of water as Bucket A?

a 2   b 5
c 6   d 10

c

18 How many semicircles are there?

a 1   b 2
c 3   d 4

b

13 Omar makes 24 ℓ of squash for a party.
He then makes 5 ℓ more squash.
How much squash does he make altogether?

a 19 ℓ   b 21 ℓ
c 25 ℓ   d 29 ℓ

d

14 Which of these has only flat surfaces?

a A rectangular box   b A banana
c A bottle   d A balloon

a

15 Miss Wood buys a violin for £287.
She had £500.
How much money does she have left?

a £213   b £287
c £313   d £387

a

16 Which of the following shows fractions arranged in the correct
order, starting from the greatest?

a $\frac{1}{4}, \frac{4}{4}, \frac{3}{4}$ b $\frac{4}{4}, \frac{1}{4}, \frac{2}{4}$

c $\frac{1}{4}, \frac{2}{4}, \frac{4}{4}$ d $\frac{4}{4}, \frac{2}{4}, \frac{1}{4}$

d

19 Which of the following is a straight line?

a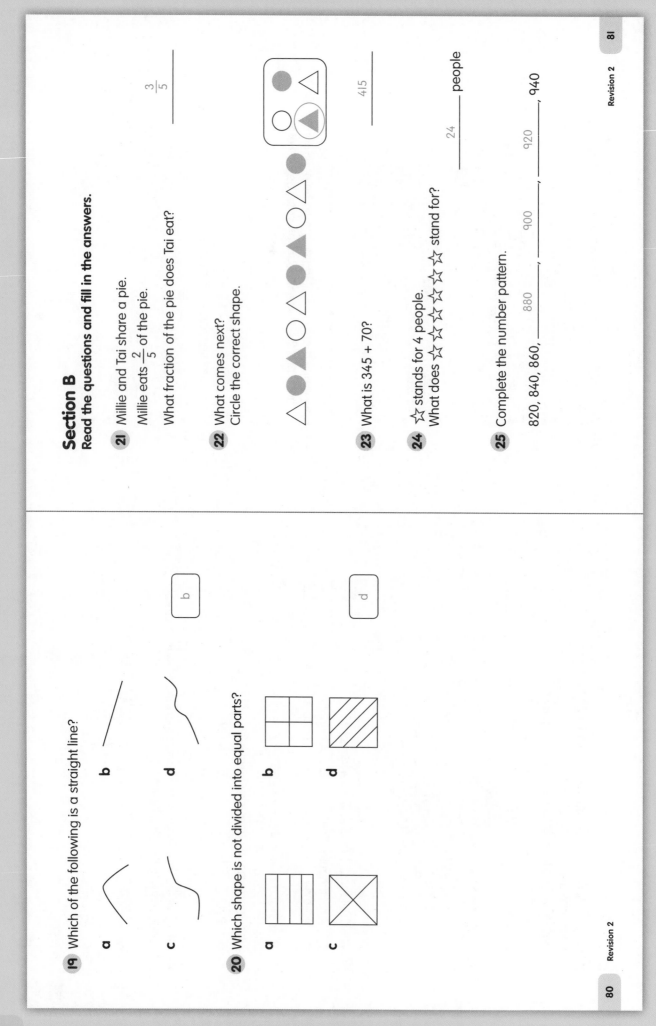

b

c

d

b

20 Which shape is not divided into equal parts?

a

b

c

d

d

Section B
Read the questions and fill in the answers.

21 Millie and Tai share a pie.
Millie eats $\frac{2}{5}$ of the pie.

What fraction of the pie does Tai eat? $\frac{3}{5}$

22 What comes next?
Circle the correct shape.

23 What is 345 + 70?   415

24 ☆ stands for 4 people.
What does ☆ ☆ ☆ ☆ ☆ ☆ stand for?   24 people

25 Complete the number pattern.

820, 840, 860, 880 , 900 , 920 , 940

26 Ruby buys two cartons of apple juice.
Each carton contains 2 litres of apple juice.
How much apple juice does Ruby buy altogether?

<u> 4 </u> litres

27 What is 920 – 80?

<u> 840 </u>

28 What fraction of the shape is shaded?

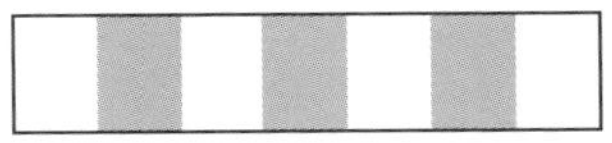

$\frac{3}{7}$

29 Draw a line 11 cm long.

30 What is 8 × 4?

<u> 32 </u>

31 What is the missing number?

789 = 7 hundreds (8) tens and 9 ones

32 Draw the hands on the clock to show 9:10.

33 Tai starts playing football at 2:00 p.m.
He finishes playing football 1 hour later.
What time does Tai finish playing football?

3:00 <u>   </u> p.m.

34 How many straight lines and curves are there?

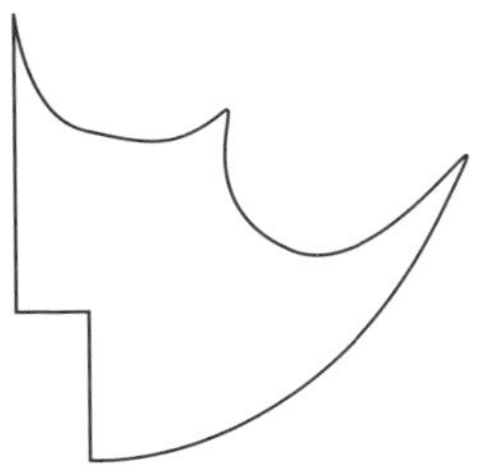

<u> 3 </u> straight lines and <u> 3 </u> curves

35 How many of each shape are there?

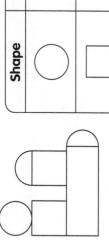

Shape	How many?
○	1
▢	2
◗	2
▭	1

36 Complete the pattern.

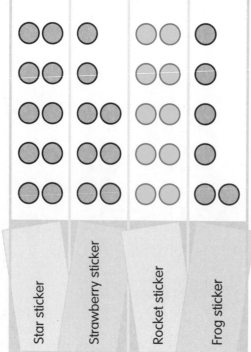

Use the graph below to answer questions **37** to **40**.

At a school fair, Millie helps on a stall that sells stickers.
The picture graph below shows the number of each type of sticker they sell.
Look at the graph. Then fill in the spaces.

Star sticker

Strawberry sticker

Rocket sticker

Frog sticker

37 Millie sells 100 star stickers.

Each ⬤ stands for _10_ stickers.

38 She sells _60_ frog stickers.

39 She sells 40 more rocket stickers than frog stickers.

She sells _100_ rocket stickers.

Complete the graph by drawing the correct number of ⬤ .

40 If she sells each sticker for £1, she will collect £ _340_ altogether.

43
Mrs Davies cuts a pizza into 12 equal parts.

Mr Davies eats $\frac{2}{12}$ of the pizza.

Mrs Davies eats $\frac{1}{12}$ of the pizza.

Their son eats $\frac{5}{12}$ of the pizza.

What fraction of the pizza do they eat altogether?

$\frac{2}{12} + \frac{1}{12} + \frac{5}{12} = \frac{8}{12}$

They eat $\frac{8}{12}$ of the pizza altogether.

44
Ella collects 189 empty cans and Hardeep collects 176 empty cans for recycling.

a Who collects more cans?

Ella collects more cans.

b How many more?

189 − 176 = 13

13 more empty cans.

Section C
Read the questions.
Show your workings in the spaces provided.

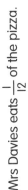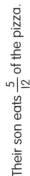

41
Miya has 6 buckets.

Each bucket holds 4 ℓ of water.

Miya fills all the buckets with water.

How many litres of water are there in the buckets altogether?

6 × 4 = 24

There are 24 ℓ of water in the buckets altogether.

42
Farha's aunt divides £30 equally among her nieces.

Each niece gets £5.

How many nieces does she have?

30 ÷ 5 = 6

She has 6 nieces.

45 There are 381 boys at Green Lane school.
There are 78 fewer girls than boys.

a   How many girls are there?

381 − 78 = 303
There are 303 girls.

b   How many girls and boys are there altogether?

381 + 303 = 684
There are 684 girls and boys altogether.

PHOTOCOPY MASTERS

Noogol

Googol

Ooogol

Koogol

Toogol

Zoogol

Unit I0: Mental Calculations

Game (Pupil Textbook 2B, p 7)

6

7

8

9

Unit 11: Money

(Pupil Textbook 2B, pp 19, 20, 21, 25 and 27)

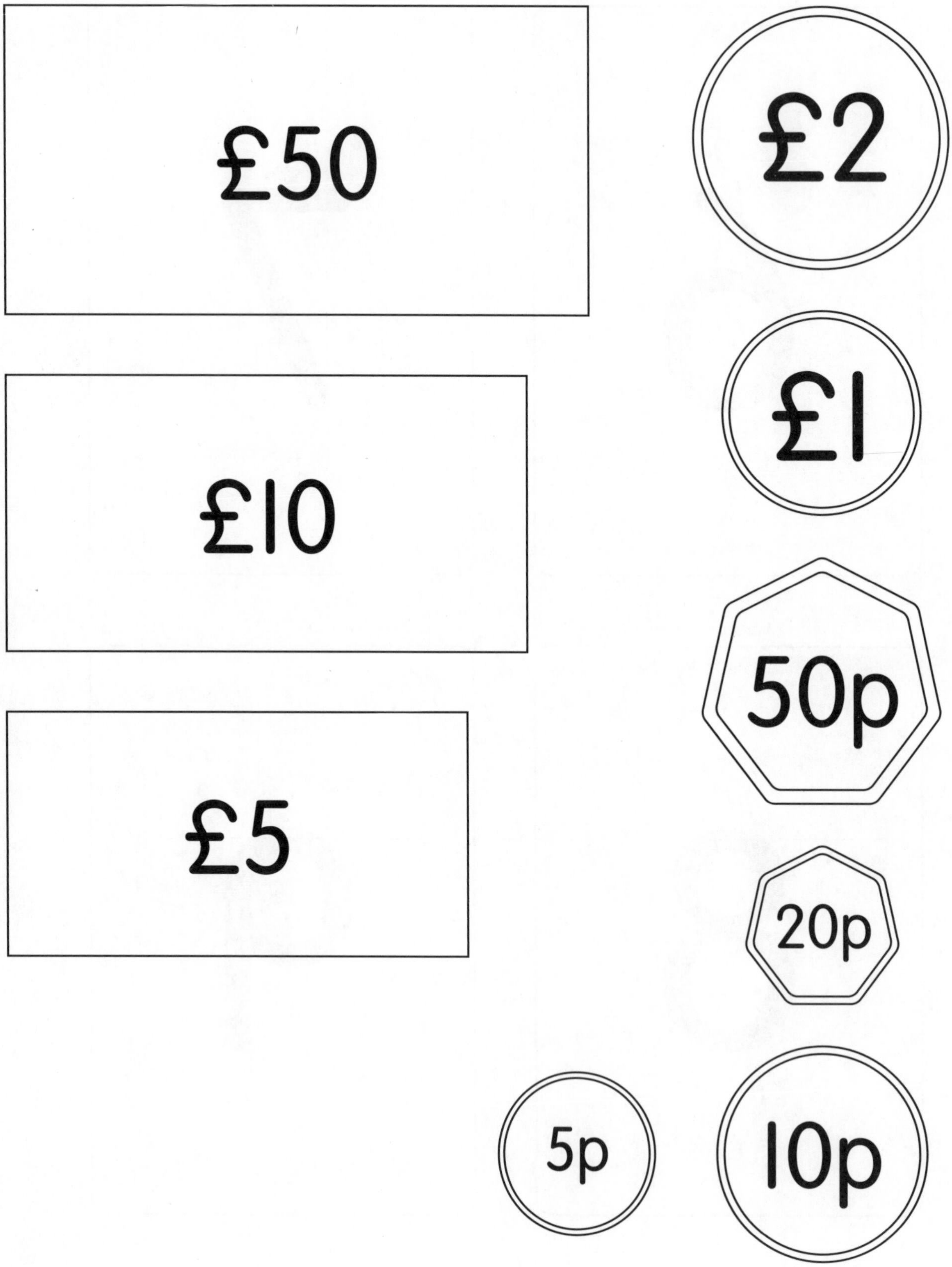

£50

£2

£10

£1

£5

50p

20p

5p

10p

Unit 12: Fractions

Let's Explore! (Pupil Textbook 2B, p 35)

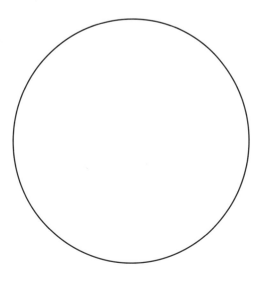

Unit 12: Fractions

Activity (Pupil Textbook 2B, p 36)

Unit 12: Fractions

Activity (Pupil Textbook 2B, p 40)

1	2	3
4	5	6

Unit 12: Fractions

Let's Explore! (Pupil Textbook 2B, p 42)

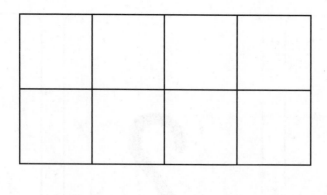

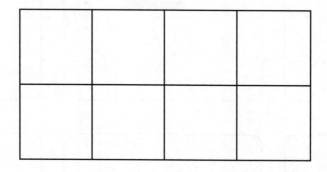

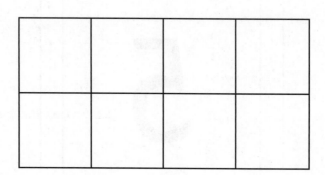

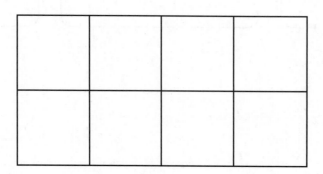

Unit 12: Fractions

Let's Explore! (Pupil Textbook 2B, p 49)

Unit 12: Fractions

Game (Pupil Textbook 2B, p 54)

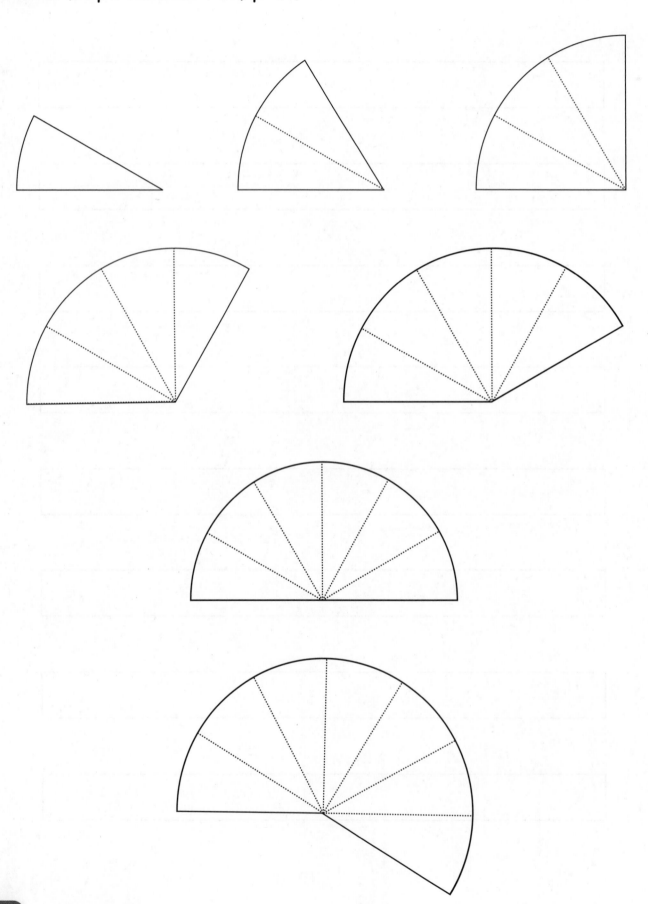

Photocopy master 8

Unit 12: Fractions

Game (Pupil Textbook 2B, p 54)

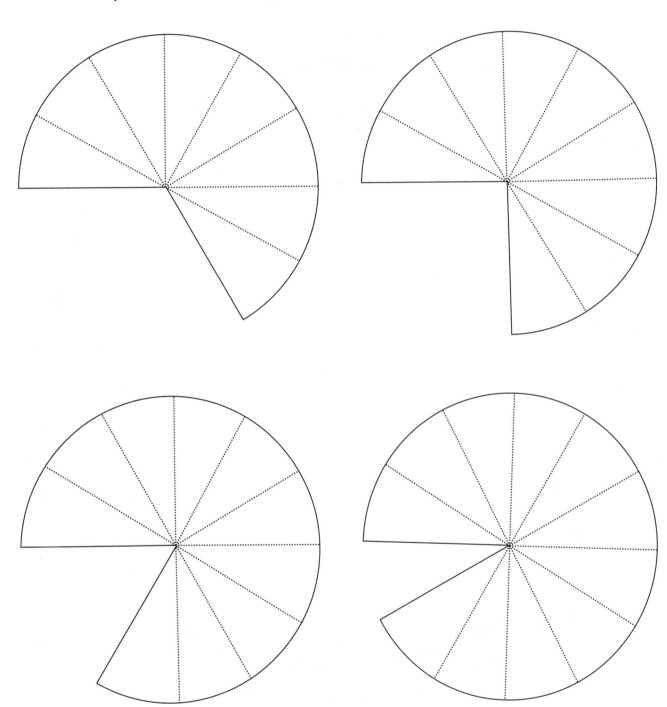

Unit 13: Time

Let's Learn! (Pupil Textbook 2B, pp 60 to 61, 62, 64, 66, 67, 69 and 74)

Unit 13: Time

Activity (Pupil Textbook 2B, p 77)

Programme	Start	End

Unit 14: Volume

Activity (Pupil Textbook 2B, p 87)

	My guess	Actual volume
A		
B		
C		

Unit 16: Lines and Surfaces

Activity (Pupil Textbook 2B, p 118)

	Number of flat surfaces
A	
B	
C	
D	
E	

Unit 16: Lines and Surfaces

Put On Your Thinking Caps! (Pupil Textbook 2B, p 119)

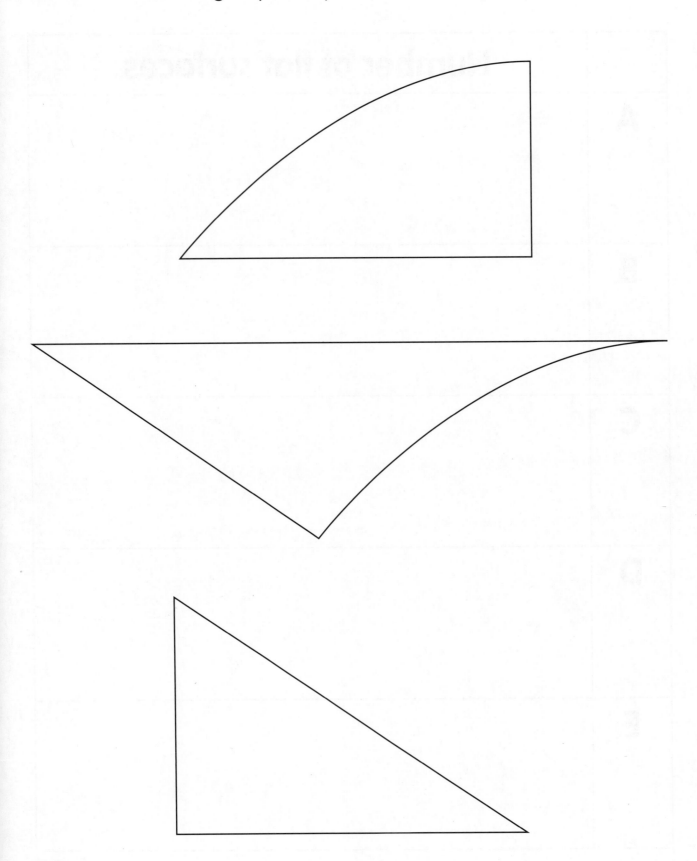

Unit 16: Lines and Surfaces

Put On Your Thinking Caps! (Pupil Textbook 2B, p 119)

Unit 17: Shapes and Patterns

Let's Learn! (Pupil Textbook 2B, p 121)

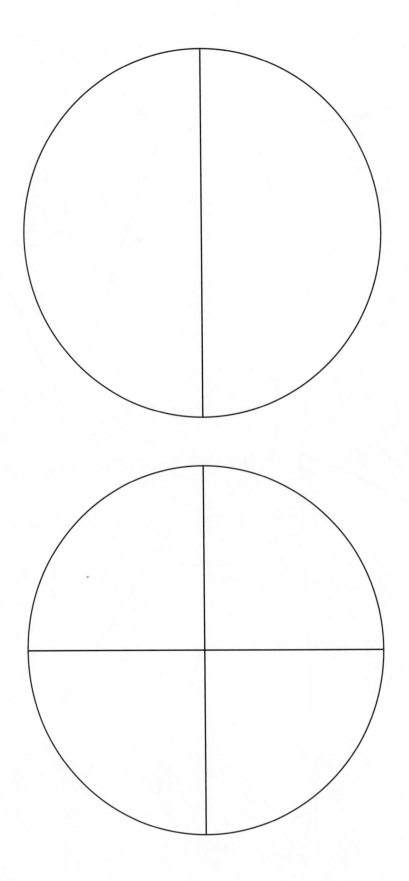

Unit 17: Shapes and Patterns

Let's Learn! (Pupil Textbook 2B, p 122)

Unit 17: Shapes and Patterns

Let's Learn! (Pupil Textbook 2B, p 122)

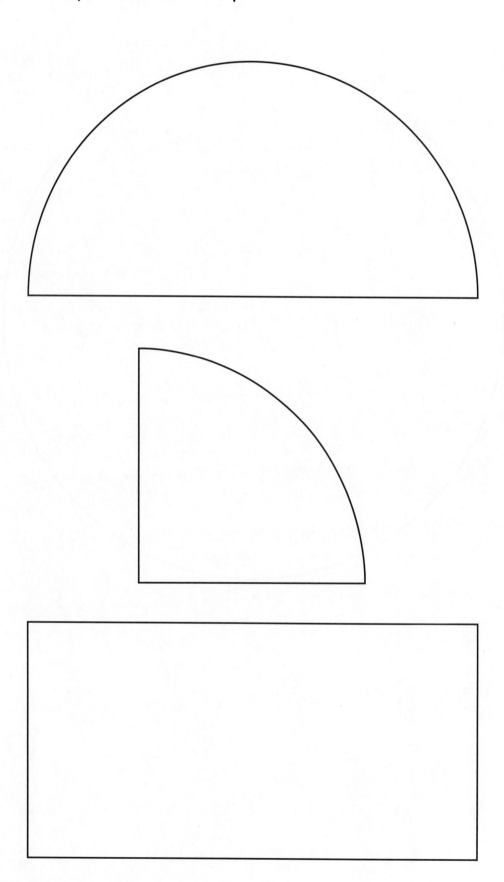

Unit 17: Shapes and Patterns

Activity (Pupil Textbook 2B, p 123)

Unit 17: Shapes and Patterns

Activity (Pupil Textbook 2B, p 123)

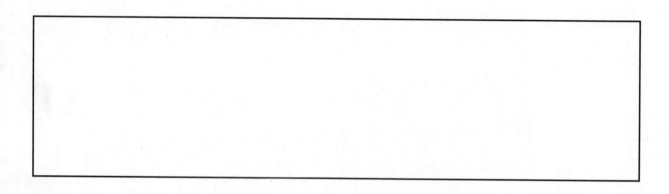

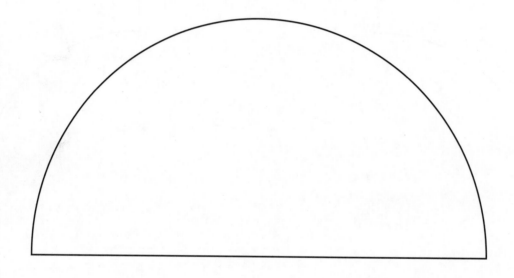

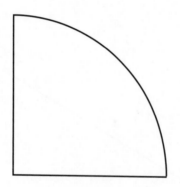

Unit 17: Shapes and Patterns

Activity (Pupil Textbook 2B, p 124)

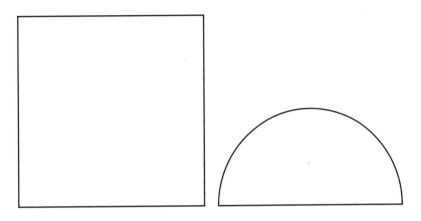

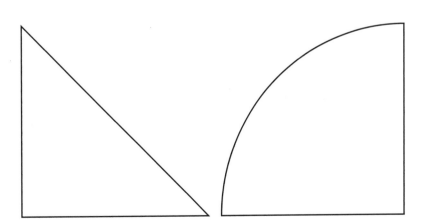

Unit 17: Shapes and Patterns

Activity (Pupil Textbook 2B, p 124)

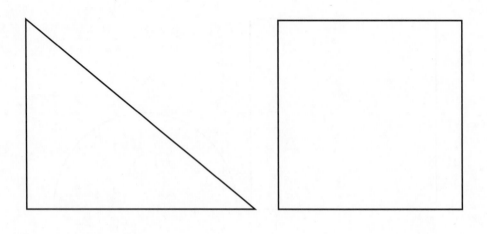

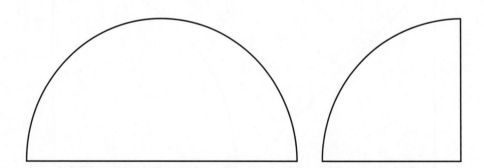

Unit 17: Shapes and Patterns

Activity (Pupil Textbook 2B, pp 126 and 128)

Unit 17: Shapes and Patterns

Activity (Pupil Textbook 2B, pp 127 and 128)

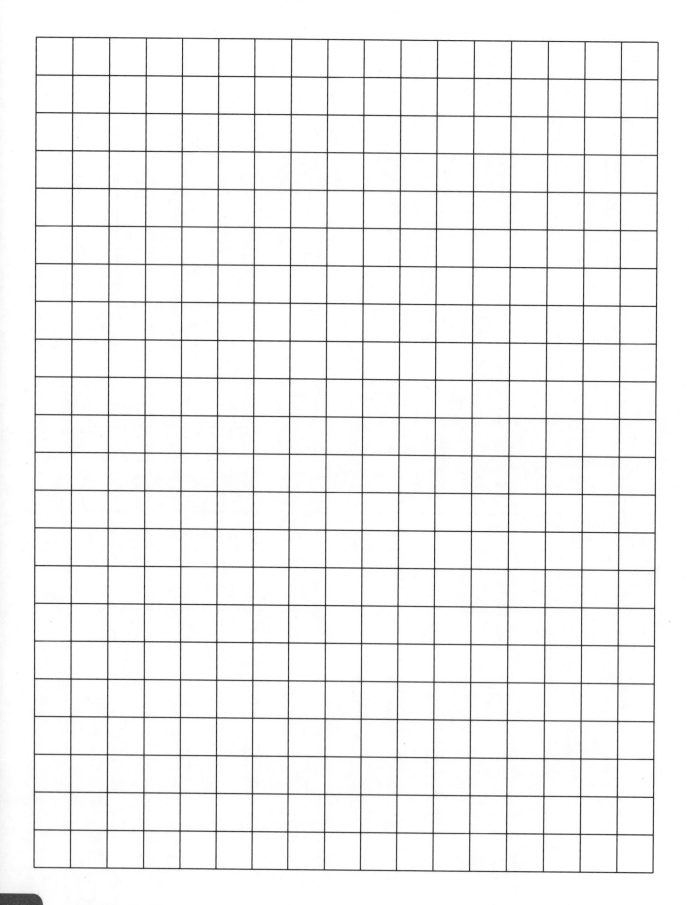

Photocopy masters

Unit 17: Shapes and Patterns

Activity (Pupil Textbook 2B, p 135)

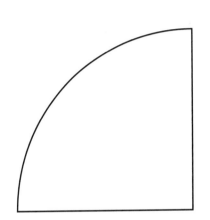
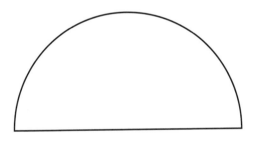

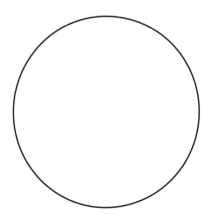
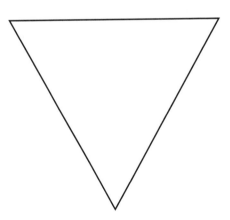

Unit 17: Shapes and Patterns

Put On Your Thinking Caps! (Pupil Textbook 2B, p 136)

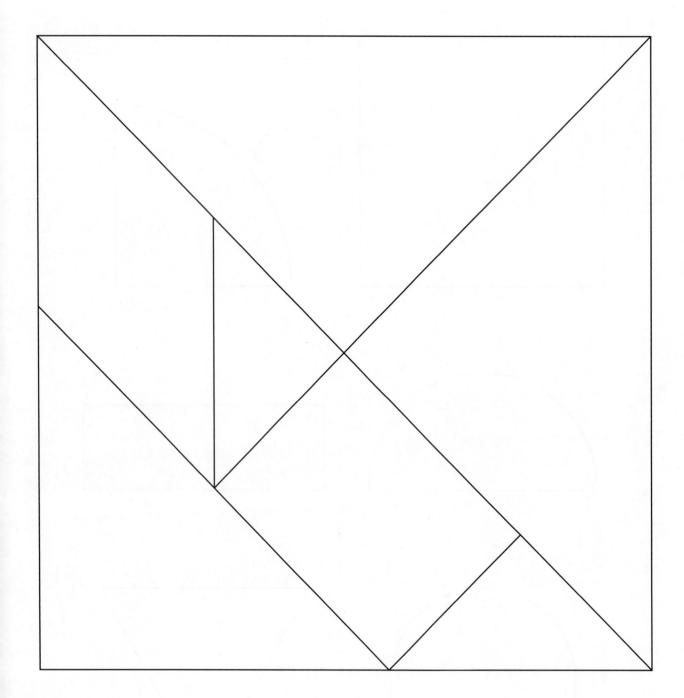